SAVE HARMLESS AGREEMENT

How to Really Save Money and Energy
in
Cooling Your House

How to Really Save Money and Energy in Cooling Your Home

George S. Barton

www.KnowledgePublications.com

Library of Congress Card N°: 78-54385

ISBN: 0-931624-00-2

www.KnowledgePublications.com

Foreword

MANY ELEMENTS of our current lifestyle were developed and grew under conditions different to those prevailing today. This is particularly true in cases involving availability and cost of energy: the way we build and drive our cars, the way we build, heat and cool our homes.

Cooling of homes is accomplished today almost exclusively by means of electric air conditioning. Just like virtually every other process or activity nowadays, air conditioning is being called upon to contribute its share of improvements in efficiency to alleviate the cost of operation, and to reduce its impact on existing and future energy shortages.

Many homeowners have done what has been preached so profusely: insulate, insulate, insulate. Some progress has also been made in the efficiency of air conditioners. Yet, homeowners continue to be faced with skyrocketing air-conditioning bills. It almost appears as if in the future the choice will be either to accept, afford, and pay for astronomical electric bills, or else to sacrifice comfort.

This needs not to be so. Yes, air conditioning will continue to be the basic tool to cool homes. Yes, electric rates are climbing and will continue to do so. We cannot eliminate entirely the air conditioner, nor can we stop the increase in electric rates by a magic trick. But we will demonstrate that there is a different way to reduce substantially the workload on the air conditioner, thereby reducing electricity consumption, without any sacrifice in comfort.

You will learn here why current methods of cooling are wasteful, and why conventional measures to save energy are mostly cosmetic. You will see a clear description of the principles and practical techniques of a method totally different from what you are using now, that may enable you to save a substantial portion of your home-cooling costs. This is the reason for the "REALLY" in the title.

Of course, the primary beneficiary of this method will be you, the user, who will see your electric bill substantially reduced. However, there are much more far-reaching consequences that would accrue to the benefit of the country as a whole if the method would be widely used, since it does not rely on the use of increasingly scarce energy supplies.

You are urged to read this book carefully, and then PUT IT TO PRACTICE. You will be amazed at the results; you will save money, and you will have the good feeling of knowing that you are helping the country to overcome the most serious dilemma it has ever faced: the problem of decreasing energy resources.

Contents

PART THREE: THE SOLUTION

PART ONE:

The Problem

1

Climate and the Human Being

or	**Danny and The Bears**

I T WAS VACATION TIME. I was with my family in Florida, and we were waiting in line to see the "Country Bear Jamboree" at Disney World. It was one of those days that earned for Florida the nickname of "Sunshine State": the sun was pounding mercilessly on the sweaty crowd waiting on that hot, humid day.

At that time, my son Danny was two years old, and you surely know that a two-year-old is not particularly prone to waiting patiently in a line-any line-not even for the Country Bear Jamboree. But the atmospheric conditions certainly did not help Danny: he was impossibly cranky, thrashing around, bothering everybody, upsetting everything. It was not easy controlling him.

Slowly, slowly, however, the line moved forward, until we finally entered the air-conditioned building. As if touched by a magic wand, within a short time Danny calmed down, and returned from acting like a caged tiger to his normal condition of just a mischievous kid.

Did you ever feel like Danny felt in the sun? Maybe you also were cranky and wanted to thrash around-except that you controlled your behavior in a more socially acceptable manner. Chances are, however, that you let off steam anyway, although you may not have been aware of it. But you, just as most other people, very likely felt that your mood, well-being, and enjoyment of life were being adversely affected by the climate. If you were at home, you may have snapped at the children, or started an argument with your spouse. If you were at work, you probably were not very productive; and if you were shopping, it is quite probable that all you wanted to do was to finish quickly and go home.

Don't feel bad; you are not alone. Hundreds of studies have confirmed time and again that there is a direct relationship between ambient conditions and mood. It is easy to appreciate the consequences of this finding, not only in our ability to enjoy our lives, but in business and industry as well. Storeowners know that a comfortable shopper is more apt to stay longer, roam around the store, be happier, and simply buy more. Time measurement studies showed early evidence of the effect of climate on factory worker productivity, and led eventually to the adoption of air conditioning in most work environments to enhance employee morale and task attitude.

Large regions of the world are subject to uncomfortably high temperatures. Not surprisingly, the distribution of population density has followed closely those climates that are pleasant and moderate. Yet, there are millions of people living in lands parched by the sun, their well-being, comfort and productivity smothered by heat. Even in the United States, the arid Southwest, one of the warmest regions in the world, became significantly populated and started on the road to prosperity only after mass-production of air conditioning equipment brought its price down to a level accessible to large segments of the population.

The point is simply this: a pleasant living and working climate is not a burgeoise whim nor a wasteful luxury. It is a legitimate aspiration of the human being toward a higher quality of life, based on well-established physiological and psychological needs. Attaining it rewards both the individual and society as a whole.

2

Climate in the United States

or   All in The Same Boat

ALTHOUGH THERE ARE A FEW COUNTRIES larger in surface area covered, no country in the world can match the diversity of climates found in the United States. From the tropical jungle of Florida to the frozen tundra of Alaska, evey conceivable combination of climatic factors are represented in our country.

Much of the United States lies in areas of normally moderate climate. However, temperatures can reach uncomfortable levels at practically every latitude. The map in Figure 1 shows that virtually every point in the contiguous 48 states is subject to having both very low temperatures in the winter as well as very high temperatures in the summer.

This fact is important. In today's social environment, the fulfillment of personal needs is almost taken for granted. The two temperature extremes mean that provisions must be made to cope with both heat and cold practically everywhere. This represents large investments in equipment for the homeowner, and even larger investments for the utilities providing energy to operate it.

A significant observation can be made in Figure 1. While the difference between the minimum recorded temperatures is very large (Caribou, at -41 to Miami or Los Angeles, at 28 makes a difference of 69 degrees) the span in maximum temperatures is much narrower (Caribou, at 96 to Bakersfield and Phoenix at 118 differ only 22 degrees).

Figure 1

EXTREME TEMPERATURES RECORDED IN SELECTED U.S. CITIES

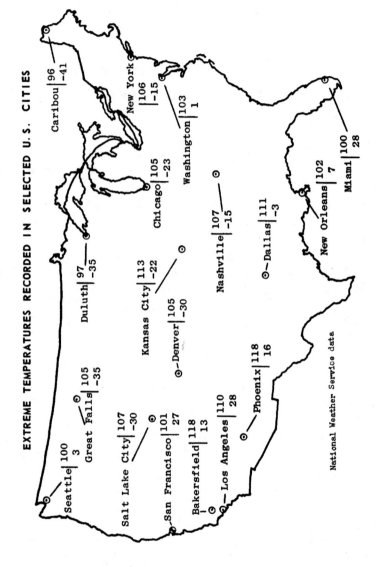

City	High	Low
Caribou	96	-41
New York	106	-15
Washington	103	1
Miami	100	28
New Orleans	102	7
Chicago	105	-23
Dallas	111	-3
Nashville	107	-15
Duluth	97	-35
Kansas City	113	-22
Denver	105	-30
Phoenix	118	16
Great Falls	105	-35
Salt Lake City	107	-30
San Francisco	101	27
Bakersfield	118	13
Los Angeles	110	28
Seattle	100	3

National Weather Service data

This means that it is much more likely that a point in a northern latitude will get uncomfortably warm, than a southern point will be very cold. Or, in simpler words, the north needs air conditioning more than the south needs heat. Conclusion: some form of home cooling is needed all over the country.

Of course, winter temperatures are milder further south, until points are reached where snow is practically unknown, and the season when below-frost temperatures may be expected is very short. This is the basic difference between the so-called "snow belt" and south of it, the snow-free region which by similarity has been dubbed "sun belt".

3

Population Shifts

or   Frypan to Fire

IT IS AN ESTABLISHED FACT that, although the majority of people do enjoy such winter sports as skiing, skating, snow-shoeing, and snowmobiling for occasional fun, an increasing segment of the population favors a mild climate for year-round living. A clear awareness of this trend is of the utmost importance for successful long-term regional planning.

People in increasing numbers seek refuge from the ravages of snow and sleet in the northern portion of the country by moving to the sun belt region. Many of these are driven by high home-heating bills. Unfortunately, a short and mild winter in the sun belt region invariably means high temperatures for a prolonged season, often from spring until fall. This in turn leads to high usage-and therefore, cost-of air conditioning.

What people moving to the sun-belt areas may not recognize is that their escape from high fuel bills for heating in the north may be substituted by equally high electricity bills to feed the air conditioner in the south. Even worse, is the real possibility that the accelerating demand for electric power needed to run the increasing number of air conditioning units may very well result in drastic measures to control their usage.

Extreme shortages of energy obviously will affect catastrophically both heating and cooling. But it appears safe to say that a moderate shortage (which is the more probable situation, at least for the foreseeable future) would affect air conditioning more than heating. This is simply because heating lends itself well to temporary supplementary measures: houses may be heated with fireplaces or wood stoves, and personal comfort may be improved by the use of warmer clothing. It even has been suggested that sleeping bags could be used as a way to save on home heating at night.

Air conditioning does not have this supplementary capability: either there is an adequate supply of electricity or there is not. The issues of air conditioning and energy are therefore tightly linked, and warrant a closer look.

4

Cooling and Energy

or　　　　　　　　**Plugging it in**

WE HAVE SEEN in the preceding section the reasons for the rapid increase in demand for air conditioning. As users, we should look into the energy impact of that demand.

Air conditioning may be powered by practically any energy source. Many gas storage tanks still greet us on the highway with reminders that "Gas cools too." Those signs were painted in the good old days of plenty, when gas utilities were vying for customers with electricity producers. Plummetting gas reserves, together with the plug-in convenience and portability of electric air conditioning units, have all but eliminated the competition, to the point that today air conditioning is almost invariably an electricity-driven utility.

Of course, the universal search for alternative sources of energy for given processes has also seen inroads of substitutes for electricity in air conditioning. One particularly interesting is solar energy, since sunshine fallout is greater in the South, where needed the most. Although solar air conditioning does exist, so far its application has been primarily in commercial installation, since its high cost virtually precludes its consideration for the average homeowner.

Electricity is a very peculiar form of energy. Its characteristics can be better appreciated by comparison to other forms of energy. In a home heated by oil, for example, a gauge indicates clearly the amount of fuel available at any given time, providing the means of planning the purchase of more oil with plenty of time. Gas utilities can measure accurately the reserves in tanks, which can be resupplied by pumping more through pipelines connected to the producing fields.

When a user turns on an electric switch, he expects that the full power necessary to operate his appliance will be available at that instant. If the scene is repeated by the millions, the overall demand may exceed the output capacity of the electricity generating machine. Electricity cannot be stored economically for use at a later date, except in few cases where elevated pumped water storage may be used. Thus, the power available becomes of lower voltage, with the consequent reduced efficiency. One sign of that reduction in efficiency is the decreased amount of light given by incandescent bulbs, thus the common term "brownout." Further reduction in voltage may have such serious consequences, including damage to users' equipment, that utilities are compelled to turn off power completely to some users so as to provide a safe voltage to the remainder. Thus, the "blackouts."

Brownouts and blackouts have been a way of life in some areas, much to the distress of the utilities, which of course would prefer to supply all that their customers require. As a helpful measure, utilities have joined in regional networks which enlarge the overall availability so as to take care of localized excesses of demand over supply.

Of course, these network schemes are successful provided that the excess demand is localized, and that the size of the excess is not so large as to surpass the capacity of the overall system. These two factors become critically thin in the summer, when heat waves may affect large areas, and consequently millions of kilowatt-gobbling air conditioners are turned on full blast at the same time.

Massive power failures under those conditions may have consequences far beyond that of damaging mechanical equipment. The blackout affecting New York City in the summer of 1977, with its sad sequel of looting and destruction, is a stern warning of the social implications of electricity availability.

No wonder, therefore, that some bizarre ideas have been developed aimed specifically at shutting off air conditioning units from remote locations. Newspapers have started carrying stories, unthinkable until recently, such as that in the accompanying article.

Utilities may shut off your air conditioner

During hot summer days in the near future Americans may find that when the air conditioner shuts down it isn't broken.

As early as next summer utilities in Michigan and Arkansas expect to be able to shut off home air conditioners when they feel they need the power elsewhere to avoid dangerous shortages.

Under such systems, companies will be able to turn off thousands of air conditioners from their headquarters to reduce the load and avoid a massive blackout such as the one that hit New York City recently.

"Eventually all utilities will have to adopt some form of automation like this" said Jeff Serfass of the U.S. Energy Research and Development Agency.

With serious doubts arising about the reliability of power during the next decade, many utilities are looking for new methods of "load management".

Building new generators is expensive and time consuming, so finding ways to reduce or restructure power usage is attractive to utilities.

Several electric companies are installing systems for remote control, and many others are considering them. The device enables the utility to cut off the air conditioner by radio or other wave method.

Customers are given credit on their bills for participating in the program.

"We are able to cut the peak off our peak load", said P. Rice, a spokesman for an Arkansas utility. "It also saves money in future generating capacity and we don't have to run more expensive equipment now".

John Hamann, president of Detroit Edison Company, agreed:

"We have found that remote control not only helps to reduce investment in generating plants by cutting peaks, but also by shifting loads to off-peak hours, we can reduce fuel costs".

The Federal Government and the Electric Power Research Institute are supporting a $7 million experimental program in San Diego, Detroit, Omaha, and Raleigh, in which remote control devices are installed.

5

Conventional Energy-Saving Tips

or   ...but I've done it !

THE PRESS AND OTHER MEDIA have given wide coverage to the subject of energy crisis. Readership interest has also led to many publications on ways to conserve energy. In addition to newspaper and periodical stories, the public utilities distribute pamphlets on how to get the most out of air conditioning. Even the Federal government, through the Department of Housing and Urban Development, has entered the mass-information market by sponsoring the preparation and distribution of a book on the subject being merchandised through retail stores.

And what do those millions and millions of words say? To be sure, there are some worthwhile recommendations. One is *insulation*. This one word has been expanded so much that entire books are dedicated to the subject, and by now practically every homeowner has become, out of necessity, an expert in insulation.

Yet, there are clear indications that insulation may have been oversold. Lured by the prospect of quick profits, insulation "experts" have mushroomed all over the country pushing their own specialty. The rush to insulate has produced widespread materials shortages, and this, in turn, has opened the opportunity to new products of unproven value and safety. A leading consumer publication has pointed out recently that additional insulation may not produce the savings promised.

Another useful piece of information, specifically regarding air conditioning, are methods recommended for calculating the

23

unit of right size and best efficiency for each individual case.

The size may be calculated with the WHILE formula. This technique requires multiplying W (the width of the room) times H (its height), times I (an insulation factor ranging from 10 to 20), times L (length of the room), times E (an exposure factor, ranging from 15 to 22). When all of these numbers are multiplied, the result, divided by 60, is the approximate optimum size air conditioner required, in BTUs.

The efficiency of an air conditioner may be measured by the EER, or Energy Efficiency Ratio. This is obtained by dividing the cooling capacity, in BTU, by the nameplate wattage needed to run it. The higher the EER, the more efficient the unit. An EER of 8 or higher is good.

Aside from these useful recommendations, most of the publications on saving energy read like a checklist to prevent only the most blatant and obvious transgressions to plain common sense. Examples:

- Use the air conditioner only when needed.
- Set it to 78°F or higher.
- Clean the filter.
- Have the unit inspected periodically.
- Don't use heat-generating appliances.
- Close blinds and drapes on the sunny side.

But one of these publications beats them all, by saying that "When taking a vacation, turn your air conditioner off before you go." This is really the most unbearable insult to the intelligence of the consumer. If the solution to our energy problems has to depend on people not forgetting to turn off their air conditioners when going on vacation, we have troubles up to our eyeballs.

Of course, all of those observations and guidelines may be useful for isolated individuals. But most homeowners are way, way past that stage: they have implemented those conventional energy-saving measures that their specific cases allowed, and have not found relief to the extent hoped for.

The time is ripe for bold measures. The time is ripe for an entirely different approach, and we will present it in later sections.

6

Energy Supply

or   **Too little , too late ?**

FOR MORE THAN TWENTY YEARS after the end of the Second World War, energy has been plentiful and inexpensive. A reflection of this is the fact that the price of electricity has declined steadily over that period, as compared to the cost of living. The energy crisis and the environmental impact of the search for new sources of energy point to the fact that a different pattern is developing, characterized by energy shortages and rising prices. Natural economic growth will continue to foster energy use. However, there are increasing economic, social and environmental pressures to make more efficient use of that energy.

Probably because of its versatility, electricity has grown more rapidly in use than other forms of energy. According to estimates of the Federal Power Commission, the demand for electric power, which in 1976 was approximately two trillion kilowatt hours, will grow to about three trillion by 1980 and will probably be double this amount by 1990. These forecasts are generally based on estimates of economic and population growth, and on the expectation that consumption will continue to grow at the same rate as in the past.

While electricity now represents only about 10 percent of the energy used in this country, it is believed that by the year 2000 the figure will reach 25 percent. This is only a 150 percent increase in its share of the energy market, but it means a 600 percent increase in demand. Air conditioning is one of the fastest growing end-uses. This is particularly burdensome on the energy

25

sources, because the efficiency of energy conversion is very poor: production of electricity from fossil fuels is about 33 percent efficient, while air conditioning itself is about 50 percent efficient. Therefore, only about 15 percent of the energy potential stored in the original fuels used to generate electricity, results in cooling energy.

The decline in the price of electricity since World War II has reverted in the early 1970's to a sharp increase in prices. This is due in part to the higher costs of fossil fuels to operate the generators, but also to the much higher price tag carried by new plants, inflated by a combination of currency depreciation, more stringent safety standards, and compliance with tougher environmental demands. Most of the additional generating capacity planned by electrical utilities will be powered by nuclear fuel, as shown in Figure 2. Vocal conservation groups are making their objections heard by the Government, resulting in additional delays and triggering gloomy forecasts.

Figure 2

ELECTRIC GENERATION
BY ENERGY RESOURCE

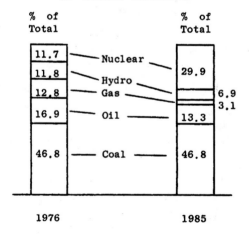

Disaster predicted
by TVA chief

The chairman of the
nation's largest power
company yesterday predicted
that the United States faces
a "disaster of major pro-
portions" unless utilities
are allowed to build more
power plants without delay.

Aubrey J. Wagner, chairman
of the Tennessee Valley
Authority, said that current
delays in the construction
of new power plants are
damaging the reliability
of electric power.He said that
the TVA sometimes has been
able to maintain its service
"with only a razor-thin margin".

Industry and government
experts recently warned that
rotating blackouts or other
restrictions on the use of
electricity are possible by
next year in the Southeast
and by 1986 in all the country.

Considerable hopes are being placed on higher prices as a way to slow the growth in energy demand. This will affect particularly electricity because the price structure currently existing in most utilities is in itself an incentive for using more: the price per kilowatt decreases as the amount of electricity used increases. The net effect of this policy is that the energy-conscious consumer subsidizes the splurge of the wasteful one. Of course, this setup cannot be changed abruptly, since many industries are currently geared to it. Sudden change might result in economic havoc and widespread unemployment.

Tax incentives have also been proposed as a way to decrease energy usage; the tax credits given homeowners for funds spent in insulating or reinsulating homes is one measure in that direction.

The real effect that all of these measures will have in reducing the gap between supply and demand for energy, and specifically electricity, is highly hypothetical. But it appears safe to say that the coming years will see an increase in the measures designed to discourage its use.

The development and promotion of energy conservation measures is just starting, and in all likelihood, the pace will accelerate in the near future. This in itself should be a warning to the homeowner for using his ingenuity and for adapting his energy-consuming utilities to the times before the next crisis strikes.

7

What do You Pay for Electricity

or   Too much , Too soon

MANY FACTORS ARE INVOLVED in determining electric rates: the type of fuel used, how old the generating plant is (and therefore, how much of it is amortized), the geographic location of the plant, and obviously how efficiently the utility is managed.

Comparison of electric rates by the kilowatt hour is very difficult because electric rate schedules have a built-in reduction in the cost per kilowatt as the total amount of electricity used increases. In other words, the first few hundred kilowatts cost a given amount; the following few hundred cost a little less; the following even less, etc. In addition, there is a fuel adjustment factor which varies according to roughly the same elements determining the basic rate. It is easy to see how these rates were developed in the time of plenty, when the energy policy, if any existed, was to push consumption. We are not far from reverting to the exact opposite.

For those reasons, the most valid comparison of electric rates are those that are made at equal kilowatt usage. Of course, a given level of usage, for example 1000 kilowatt-hour monthly, may be exorbitant in an area with low air conditioning use, whereas it might be very common in a southern location.

Table 1 shows the comparative cost of typical residential 500 kilowatt hour bills in certain selected cities. It illustrates the wide difference that can be found in such varied locations.

29

TABLE 1

COST OF 500 KILOWATT-HOURS OF ELECTRICITY
IN SELECTED MAJOR U.S. CITIES

CITY	JULY 1977 ($)
Cleveland	26.20
New York City	51.19
Madison	23.79
Newark	32.79
Fort Wayne	21.78
Cincinnati	20.65
Buffalo	19.68
District of Columbia	22.22
Albuquerque	20.22
Wilmington	29.31
Philadelphia	28.15
Milwaukee	18.75
Salt Lake City	21.34
Allentown	21.68
Detroit	23.08
Baltimore	23.54
Huntington	16.68
Denver	17.42
Flint	19.38

Table 2, on the other hand, shows the ten highest and the ten lowest average residential 500 kilowatt hour bills. Note that the Pacific Northwest locations have the lowest rates. This is a direct consequence of the fact that most utilities in that area utilize a high proportion of hydroelectric power to generate their electricity.

TABLE 2

TEN HIGHEST AND LOWEST RESIDENTIAL ELECTRIC
BILLS, BY CITY--APRIL 1, 1977
(500 KILOWATT-HOURS)

HIGHEST		LOWEST	
City	Bills	City	Bills
New York City, New York	43.29	Spokane, Washington	7.95
Middletown, New York	36.16	Lewiston, Idaho	8.30
Fitchburg, Massachusetts	35.11	Yakima, Washington	10.70
Mahwah, New Jersey	34.38	Bellevue, Washington	11.62
Rutland, Vermont	33.17	Cheyenne, Wyoming	11.99
Wilmington, Delaware	32.54	Casper, Wyoming	12.82
Newark, New Jersey	31.78	Billings, Montana	12.86
Salem, New Hampshire	30.87	Ontario, Oregon	13.00
Kingston, Pennsylvania	30.73	Boise, Idaho	13.42
Providence, Rhode Island	29.68	Portland, Oregon	13.62

On a more local scale, Table 3 presents a breakdown of 500 and 1000 kilowatt hour residential bills by state and individual utility. The approximate cost of kilowatt hour for the particular level of use can be calculated by dividing the amount in dollars by the corresponding number of kilowatt hours shown.

Tables 1, 2, and 3 have been compiled from data contained in a report on residential electric utility bills published by the National Association of Regulatory Utility Commissioners, Washington, D.C.

TABLE 3

RESIDENTIAL ELECTRIC UTILITY BILLS
July 1, 1977

(in Dollars)

	500 kWh	1000 kWh
Alabama		
Alabama Power Company	23.43	43.85
Arizona		
Tucson Gas & Electric Co.	27.90	48.69
Arizona Public Service Co.	26.72	48.57
Salt River Project	25.79	44.65
Arkansas		
Arkansas Power & Light Co.	24.90	44.05
Arkansas-Missouri Power Co.	27.46	49.71
Southwestern Electric Power Co.	17.17	32.11
California		
San Diego Gas & Electric Co.	22.01	42.24
Southern California Edison Co.	20.87	37.91
Pacific Gas & Electric Co.	17.48	39.25
Los Angeles Dept. of Water & Power	23.59	42.73
Colorado		
Public Service Company of Colorado	17.42	33.66
Southern Colorado Power Co.	19.49	35.38
Home Light & Power Company	19.01	32.51
Connecticut		
Connecticut Light & Power Company	25.52	42.59
Hartford Electric Light Company	27.11	47.52
United Illuminating Company	27.50	51.41
Delaware		
Delmarva Power & Light Co.	29.31	51.62

	500 kWh	1000 kWh
District of Columbia		
Potomac Electric Power Co.	22.22	49.45
Florida		
Florida Power & Light Co.	20.86	39.80
Florida Power Corporation	24.21	45.18
Tampa Electric Co.	23.04	41.68
Gulf Power Company	21.32	38.70
Georgia		
Georgia Power Company	18.01	35.24
Savannah Electric & Power Co.	26.59	47.77
Hawaii		
Maui Electric Company, Ltd.	34.45	62.30
Kauai Electric Company	37.84	68.92
Hawaiian Electric Company, Inc.	25.18	45.46
Hawaii Electric Light Co., Inc.	37.71	65.72
Idaho		
Idaho Power Company	14.60	22.19
Washington Water Power Co.	9.00	15.40
Utah Power & Light Co.	19.70	35.20
Illinois		
Central Illinois Light Co.	25.74	51.69
Central Illinois Public Service Co.	24.55	45.16
Commonwealth Edison Co.	21.58	40.71
Illinois Power Co.	21.78	41.15
Iowa-Illinois Gas & Electric Co.	24.17	44.55
Union Electric Co.	20.76	39.45
Indiana		
Indiana & Michigan Electric Co.	21.78	35.93
Indianapolis Power & Light Co.	19.57	31.19
Northern Indiana Public Service Co.	22.74	42.15
Public Service of Indiana Inc.	22.04	35.85
Southern Indiana Gas & Electric Co.	19.31	34.94

	500 kWh	1000 kWh
Iowa		
Interstate Power Company	21.90	39.91
Iowa-Illinois Gas & Electric Co.	24.61	45.52
Iowa Electric Light & Power Co.	24.35	44.42
Iowa Power & Light Co.	23.44	43.02
Iowa Southern Utilities Co.	20.48	38.81
Union Electric Co.	18.65	35.54
Iowa Public Service Co.	25.74	47.61
Kansas		
Central Kansas Power Co.	19.16	33.22
Central Telephone & Utilities Co.	21.70	38.83
Kansas City Power & Light Co.	20.78	37.21
Kansas Power & Light Co.	19.42	37.51
Empire District Electric Co.	17.26	32.04
Kansas Gas & Electric Co.	18.77	34.22
Kentucky		
Kentucky Power Company	16.59	27.74
Kentucky Utilities Company	18.43	32.08
Louisville Gas & Electric Co.	17.34	32.18
Union Light, Heat & Power Co.	20.76	36.49
Louisiana		
Central Louisana Electric Co.	20.47	37.19
Gulf States Utilities Co.	19.68	33.51
Louisiana Power & Light Co.	16.30	27.71
Southwestern Electric Power Co.	16.24	30.40
Maine		
Central Maine Power Co.	20.66	35.76
Bangor Hydro-Electric Co.	23.79	39.36
Maine Public Service Co.	25.45	43.00
Maryland		
Baltimore Gas & Electric Co.	23.54	41.60
Potomac Electric Power Co.	27.66	51.20
Delmarva Power & Light Co.	27.60	47.11
The Potomac Edison Co.	18.98	34.08

	500 kWh		1000 kWh
Massachusetts			
Massachusetts Electric Co.	29.92	......	57.12
Boston Edison Co.	31.01	......	65.57
Cambridge Electric Light Co.	27.33	......	49.78
Brockton Edison Co.	26.93	......	47.48
Western Massachusetts Electric Co.	29.77	......	49.92
New Bedford Gas & Light Co.	30.17	......	54.31
Fall River Electric Light Co.	26.90	......	49.10
Fitchburg Gas & Electric Co.	33.88	......	60.14
Nantucket Electric Co.	37.85	......	65.28
Manchester Electric Co.	33.64	......	64.29
Michigan			
Detroit Edison Company	23.08	......	45.16
Consumers Power Company	19.38	......	37.27
Minnesota			
Interstate Power Company	23.34	......	42.01
Otter Tail Power Company	25.20	......	37.25
Northern States Power Company	27.00	......	51.50
Minnesota Power & Light Company	24.40	......	40.51
Mississippi			
Mississippi Power & Light Co.	24.40	......	40.51
Mississippi Power Co.	19.66	......	33.92
Missouri			
Arkansas-Missouri Power Co.	20.89	......	36.91
Citizens Electric Corp.	18.67	......	34.95
Empire District Electric Co.	19.65	......	36.66
Kansas City Power & Light Co.	21.40	......	38.09
Missouri Edison Co.	26.17	......	44.51
Missouri Power & Light Co.	21.37	......	37.20
Missouri Public Service Co.	26.82	......	47.00
Missouri Utilities Co.	23.41	......	41.26
St. Joseph Light & Power Co.	26.39	......	45.82
Union Electric Co.	19.45	......	36.93
Montana			
The Montana Power Company	12.86	......	20.86
Montana-Dakota Utilities Co.	17.23	......	32.45

	500 kWh	1000 kWh

Nevada
Nevada Power Company	15.31	28.61
Sierra Pacific Power Co.	16.31	32.27

New Hampshire
Concord Electric Co.	24.48	42.30
Connecticut Valley Electric Co.	27.34	49.66
Exeter & Hampton Electric Co.	25.68	45.18
Granite State Electric Co.	31.82	59.87
New Hampshire Electric Coop.	26.82	47.47
Public Service of New Hampshire	25.80	45.60

New Jersey
Atlantic City Electric Co.	28.58	52.85
Public Service Electric & Gas Co.	32.79	62.98
Jersey Central Power & Light Co.	34.45	63.52
Rockland Electric Co.	37.84	70.05

New Mexico
Community Public Service Co.	21.20	38.39
El Paso Electric Co.	20.86	39.83
New Mexico Electric Co.	19.07	35.11
Public Service Company of New Mexico	20.22	36.28
Southwestern Public Service Co.	22.09	40.69

New York
Central Hudson Gas & Electric Corp.	27.48	49.00
Consolidated Edison of New York	51.19	99.67
Long Island Lighting Co.	32.03	61.83
New York State Electric & Gas Corp.	21.01	37.85
Niagara Mohawk Power Corp.	19.68	33.58
Orange & Rockland Utilities, Inc.	38.40	71.56
Rochester Gas & Electric Corp.	22.13	38.46

North Carolina
Virginia Electric & Power Co.	23.35	44.72
Nantahala Power & Light Co.	18.12	29.19
Carolina Power & Light Co.	22.22	38.75
Duke Power Co.	17.77	33.53

	500 kWh	1000 kWh

North Dakota
Montana-Dakota Utilities Co.	22.06	40.63
Northern States Power Co.	19.89	36.78
Otter Tail Power Co.	21.25	39.10

Ohio
Cincinnati Gas & Electric Co.	20.65	36.21
Cleveland Electric Ill. Co.	26.20	51.11
Columbus & Southern Ohio Co.	22.59	42.45
Dayton Power & Light Co.	21.28	35.74
Ohio Edison Co.	25.00	43.01
Ohio Power Co.	18.69	32.89
Toledo Edison Co.	24.90	46.01

Oklahoma
| Oklahoma Gas & Electric Co. | 19.25 | 35.23 |
| Public Service of Oklahoma | 21.08 | 40.94 |

Oregon
Portland General Electric Co.	13.95	25.15
Pacific Power & Light Co.	12.88	23.50
California-Pacific Utilities Co.	14.91	26.06

Pennsylvania
Duquesne Light Co.	27.26	51.38
Metropolitan Edison Co.	26.49	49.37
Pennsylvania Electric Co.	27.38	46.56
Pennsylvania Power Co.	20.64	34.03
Pennsylvania Power & Light Co.	21.68	35.96
Philadelphia Electric Co.	28.15	58.24
West Penn Power Co.	20.37	36.11
UGI Corp.--Luzerne Electric	29.99	47.06
West Penn Power Co.	19.41	33.80

Rhode Island
| Narragansett Electric Co. | 30.07 | 55.36 |
| Blackstone Valley Electric Co. | 24.24 | 42.53 |

	500 kWh	1000 kWh

South Carolina
South Carolina Electric & Gas Co. .... 24.05 ...... 42.25
Duke Power Company .... 17.49 ...... 34.56
Carolina Power & Light Co. .... 21.38 ...... 36.77

Tennessee
Kingsport Power Company .... 16.49 ...... 27.91

Texas
Houston Lighting & Power Co. .... 23.87 ...... 35.36

Utah
Utah Power & Light Co. .... 21.34 ...... 38.25
California-Pacific Utilities Co. .... 17.67 ...... 32.52

Vermont
Central Vermont Public Service .... 17.25 ...... 28.74
Green Mountain Power Co. .... 22.12 ...... 43.12

Virginia
Appalachian Power Co. .... 18.97 ...... 32.01
Potomac Edison Co. .... 20.87 ...... 37.70
Virginia Electric & Power Co. .... 25.53 ...... 48.83

Washington
Washington Water Power Co. .... 8.17 ...... 13.74
Pacific Power & Light Co. .... 10.10 ...... 18.41
Puget Sound Power & Light Co. .... 10.95 ...... 18.45

West Virginia
Appalachian Power Co. .... 16.68 ...... 28.23
Monongahela Power Co. .... 22.97 ...... 38.94

Wisconsin
Lake Superior District Power Co. .... 20.83 ...... 38.65
Madison Gas & Electric Co. .... 23.79 ...... 45.58
Northern States Power Co. .... 17.37 ...... 30.07
Superior Water, Light & Power Co. .... 19.70 ...... 35.70
Wisconsin Electric Power Co. .... 18.75 ...... 30.74
Wisconsin Michigan Power Co. .... 18.25 ...... 29.15
Wisconsin Power & Light Co. .... 20.65 ...... 37.80
Wisconsin Public Servic Corp. .... 22.46 ...... 40.44

8

How to Build a Graph

or   One Picture is worth a Thousand Guesses

YOU HAVE SEEN THEM in the business section of your newspaper. You have seen them in the hospital, when they kept
track of your temperature. You have seen them when
reading about the Cost of Living Index. We are talking
about graphs, or charts, those marvelous figures that tell you how
things change.

Why not use graphs to find out how your electric usage
changes during the year? In the following sections, you will be
surprised to see just how much you can learn from having your
electric consumption plotted on a graph. So, let's see how to
construct one.

The procedure is very simple. Start by putting in order
all your electric bills for the number of years you wish to cover;
usually five years will give you a good idea of trends. If you
have not kept your bills, you can get the necessary figures by
requesting them in writing from the Billing Department of your
utility. Make sure you request to have the figures by date, in
both kilowatt-hours and dollars. Some utilities tend to bill
periodically estimated or two-month averaged figures rather than
monthly meter readings. You can use those figures, since the
purpose of the graph is to find trends over a much longer period
of time.

Figure   3

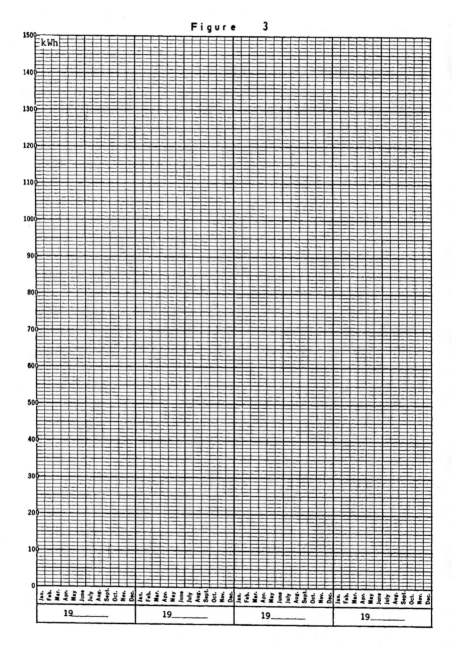

Either with your retained bills or with the figures obtained from the utility, you can now prepare a table such as the following hypothetical example:

Year	Period Ending	kWh	$
197...	January 16	374	22.95
	February 16	580	30.55
	March 17	388	23.47
	April 15	362	21.55
	May 17	542	39.57
	June 16	760	52.16
	July 18	890	65.23
	August 16	700	48.83
	September 15	550	39.78
	October 17	390	24.32
	November 16	481	28.66
	December 15	496	29.92

And so on for other years.

Now you are ready to start constructing your graphs. Let's start with Figure 3. For this, we will need the columns headed "Period Ending" and "kWh." On the vertical scale, find a point close to 374. (Since the paper has low resolution, estimate halfway between 350 and 400.) Now take an envelope (a sheet of paper with a straight edge works fine too) and place it so that its sides are parallel to the lines of the blank figure, and the lower edge is close to the point representing 374, as shown in Figure 5.

Next, take another envelope, and place it vertically so that its left edge is aligned with the first mark of the horizontal scale, which will represent January; now make a dot at the intersecting corner (Figure 6).

Repeat the procedure for the 580 kWh of February, etc., etc., until you have made a dot for each month. Now with a ruler, draw straight lines between consecutive dots, and you have the graph made.

The procedure for building the graph in Figure 4 is exactly the same, except that the columns to be used are "Period Ending" and "$."

Go ahead and complete Figures 3 and 4 for your home. We'll use them later.

41

Figure 4

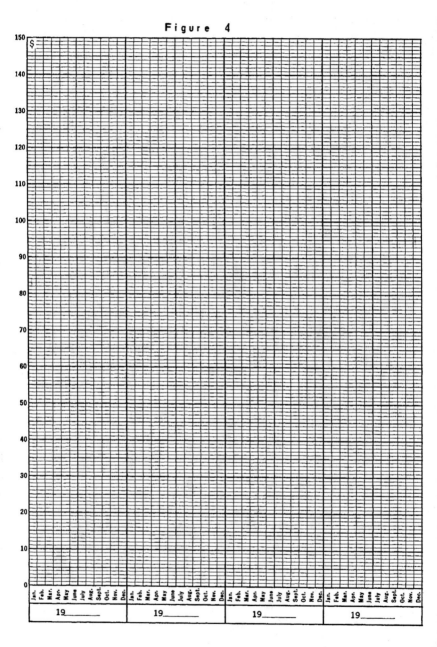

BUILDING A GRAPH

Figure 5

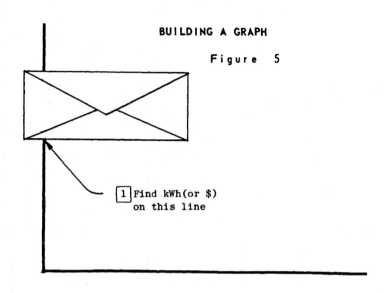

1 Find kWh(or $)
on this line

Figure 6

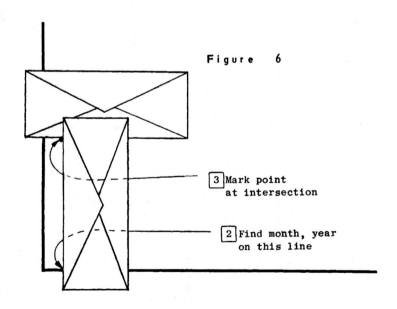

3 Mark point
at intersection

2 Find month, year
on this line

www.KnowledgePublications.com

9

Figure Your Cost

or   Too much , continued

THE SURPRISE AND AMAZEMENT that homeowners have been experiencing every time they receive a new electric bill has become so proverbial that now it is even celebrated in cartoons.

But really it is not funny. Especially not for those homeowners who have made the effort and investment required to comply with the conventional energy-saving measures that we reviewed, touted as the cure of the energy cost worries.

You can get considerable insight and a better understanding of where your energy dollar goes if you plot charts both in kilowatt-hours used and in dollars billed, as we saw in the previous section.

Let us take, for example, Figures 7 and 8, which were built following exactly the directions in Section 8. These are typical shape curves for a home with electric air conditioning but fossil-fuel (gas or oil) heating. Of course, the level of the curves may be higher or lower depending on the size of the house, number and type of appliances, percentage of time used, etc. But you should be able to draw "base lines" as shown, averaging the usage during the months that the air conditioner is NOT used. This base line will tell you what your usage of electricity is for operating lighting, the washer, dryer, tools, etc. The kilowatt base line may be horizontal if you have not had significant changes; it may go up if you have been adding lighting, outlets or

45

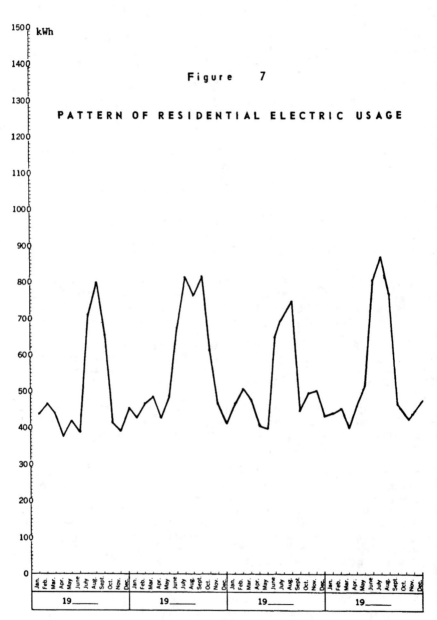

Figure 7

PATTERN OF RESIDENTIAL ELECTRIC USAGE

46

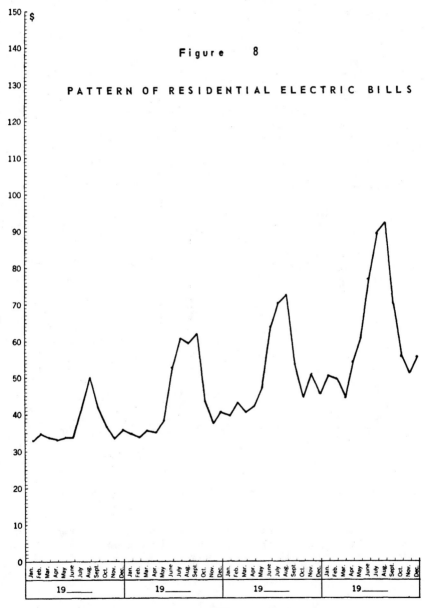

Figure 8

PATTERN OF RESIDENTIAL ELECTRIC BILLS

appliances, or it may go down, for example, if your children left for college. The dollar base line, in all probability, will go up, and considerably faster than your kilowatt base line.

Of course, if the whole house is electrically heated, or there is another large seasonal usage of electricity, this will show as peaks at the appropriate months. Disregard them in drawing the base lines.

To draw the base lines, examine the graphs you made in Section 8. You will see that there is a bunch of peaks and valleys. Some of the peaks will go much higher than the preceding months. You will be able to recognize, by the month of the year, that this is about the time you start using air conditioning. Now try to position a transparent ruler so that the straight edge about averages the ups and downs of the months NOT representing air conditioner use. Draw a line.

To calculate the amount of kWh and dollars attributable to air conditioners, let's refer to Figure 9. This is simply the curve for one year, on a larger scale.

From the graph you can see that the base line is about $27. Now we subtract this amount from the various bills:

Month	Bill $	Less Base Line $	Difference (Attributable to Air Conditioning) $
May	39.57	27	12.57
June	52.16	27	25.16
July	65.23	27	38.23
August	48.83	27	21.83
September	39.78	27	12.78
		TOTAL $:	110.57

This was your approximate cost for air conditioning during that year.

Don't be surprised if in some year you had a much higher or much lower than average air conditioning cost (as shown in Figure 7). If you think back, very probably you will be able to remember that in that year the summer was particularly hot or mild, or that your relatives from Canada spent a month at your house, or you took your family for a vacation to the beach. To compensate for these variations, add the total air conditioning costs for the years of your graph, and divide by the number of years considered: the result is your annual average consumption of electricity for air conditioning.

Figure 9

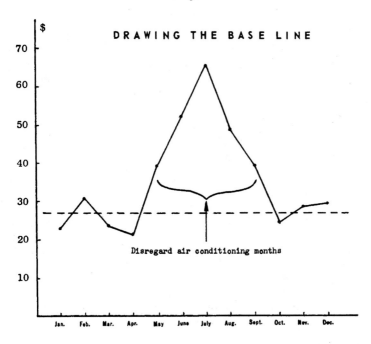

10

Compare Your Cost

or   Are You in line ?

YOU CAN FIND OUT how the annual consumption figure which you just calculated compares with other homes in your area or any other place in the country. If you live in a development where there are many houses just like yours, you can compare the effectiveness of your air conditioning system or your insulation to that of your neighbors'. Likewise, you can calculate approximately how much it would cost to provide air conditioning to your house if it was located in a number of hypothetical places. You may use the following procedure, which gives approximate results.

Years of experience have provided statistical data on the number of load hours that an average home requires for maintaining comfortable temperatures during a normal season. This will incorporate not only the climate factors described before, but the cooling habits of the particular regions.

Based on those numbers, maps such as that shown in Figure 10 have been developed. Lines connect locations using approximately the same number of hours of full operation air conditioning per year. Of course these lines necessarily represent averages of ranges which can be fairly wide, as shown in Table 4.

These figures may be utilized to calculate the requirements for electric power of a home and how much it will cost. Since you obviously do not have exact data on the number of hours that other people run their air conditioner, you will have to

51

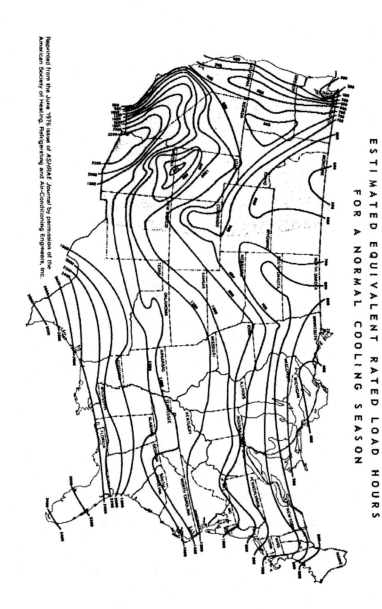

Figure 10

ESTIMATED EQUIVALENT RATED LOAD HOURS FOR A NORMAL COOLING SEASON

Reprinted from the June 1976 issue of *ASHRAE Journal* by permission of the American Society of Heating, Refrigerating and Air-Conditioning Engineers, Inc.

eyeball a value from the map. Also, you don't have the wattage rating of somebody else's air conditioner, but you can use your own as a first approximation. The following form may be used for that purpose:

APPROXIMATE COMPUTATION

OF AIR CONDITIONING COSTS

a)   Estimated number of hours (from map)   :

b)   Kilowatt rating of the air conditioner :

c)   Annual kilowatt hour consumed (a x b) :

d)   Electric rate , ¢/kWh (from Table 3) :

e)   Annual cost of operating
air conditioner (c x d)   :

Table 4

ESTIMATED EQUIVALENT RATED LOAD HOURS FOR SELECTED CITIES

	Hours		Hours
Albuquerque, NM	800-2200	Indianapolis, IN	600-1600
Atlantic City, NJ	500-800	Little Rock, AR	1400-2400
Birmingham, AL	1200-2200	Minneapolis, MN	400-800
Boston, MA	400-1200	New Orleans, LA	1400-2800
Burlington, VT	200-600	New York, NY	500-1000
Charlotte, NC	700-1100	Newark, NJ	400-900
Chicago, IL	500-1000	Oklahoma City, OK	1100-2000
Cleveland, OH	400-800	Pittsburgh, PA	900-1200
Cincinnati, OH	1000-1500	Rapid City, SD	800-1000
Columbia, SC	1200-1400	St. Joseph, MO	1000-1600
Corpus Christi, TX	2000-2500	St. Petersburg, FL	1500-2700
Dallas, TX	1200-1600	San Diego, CA	800-1700
Denver, CO	400-800	Savannah, GA	1200-1400
Des Moines, IA	600-1000	Seattle, WA	400-1200
Detroit, MI	700-1000	Syracuse, NY	200-1000
Duluth, MN	300-500	Trenton, NJ	800-1000
El Paso, TX	1000-1400	Tulsa, OK	1500-2200
Honolulu, HI	1500-3500	Washington, DC	700-1200

Reprinted by permission from
the 1976 Systems volume
of ASHRAE Handbook &
Product Directory.

PART TWO:

The Basics

11

Transmission of Heat

or   Tennis , anyone ?

ALTHOUGH OUR INTENTION is to use non-technical language in this book, the method to save in home cooling costs that we'll describe later would be appreciated better if some simple facts about the physics of heat are clearly understood.

We will start with Transmission of Heat, because this is really what the whole problem of home cooling is all about. Which brings us to defining an average home. This is not as hard as it may look. There are millions of houses in the U.S., and probably thousands of house styles. However, for the purpose of describing what happens to a house on a summer day, let us select the Smith's home.

The Smiths live in a house (Figure 11) that has two levels usable for normal activities with adults standing up, and a space under the gable roof that we shall call attic. In some homes this attic is high enough so that an adult can walk normally, while in some others an adult would have to crawl on hands and knees, thus, the name of crawl space. The upper living area has the bedrooms, while the lower includes the family room.

The Smith's home was built before 1973, the year of the big energy shortage. This is why it had just three inches of fiber-glass insulation on the attic floor, that is, between the attic and the upper living area. Although the Smiths call their home a bi-level (probably because the floor of the lower level is about

57

Figure 11

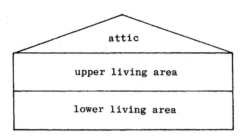

```
                    attic

               upper living area

               lower living area
```

flush with the ground), they know that their friends, the McKeons, have a very similar house layout. The major difference is that the floor of the lower level is below grade, so that the surrounding ground comes at about the division between the upper and lower areas. Still, the bedrooms, kitchen, etc., are upstairs, while the other level downstairs, the basement, may or may not be finished. The McKeons call their home a ranch.

No doubt, you can identify many variations of this general layout: raised ranches, split-levels, etc., etc. Whichever way it is called, you certainly have found out that the lower level of a house is usually the coolest on a summer day, especially if it is mostly below grade, as in the case of a ranch. This is why we will be concerned primarily with what happens to the upper living area and attic.

We know that a house may be pleasantly cool in the early morning hours of a summer day, but, as the temperature increases during the day, somehow heat comes from the outside of the house to the inside. This happens even if all doors and windows are kept tightly closed (Figure 12). What air conditioning does is simply to reverse the process, and make the heat go back from the inside of the house to the outside.

Figure 12

TEMPERATURES IN THE HOME
IN A SUMMER DAY

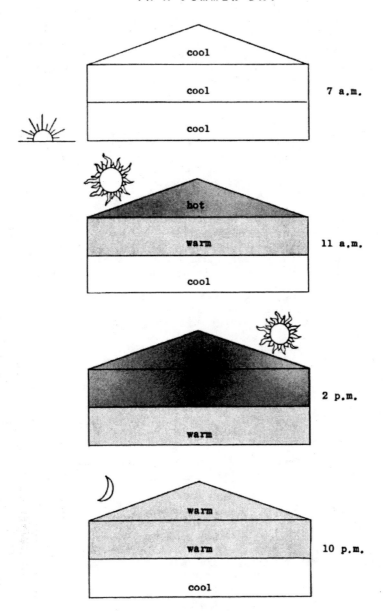

Thus, we have reached by a simple description of the process of home cooling the definition of what heat transfer, any heat transfer, really is: it is the migration of heat from a warmer place to a cooler place. Note that we purposely use a comparative word, warmer or cooler, not hot or cold, because in heat transfer we are always dealing with relative conditions of temperature. Even a place which is "cool" by one standard, will appear "warm," if we compare it with another place which is at a much lower temperature.

These simple concepts actually represent one of the most fundamental laws of physics: that in order for heat transfer to occur, there must be a difference of temperature; and that the direction of spontaneous transfer of heat is always from warmer to colder places. Another important principle to keep in mind is that the larger the difference in temperatures between the warmer and cooler place, the faster heat transfer will occur.

The migration of heat from a warmer place to a cooler place may occur by three modes: Radiation, Conduction, and Convection. You might be amazed to hear this, but the truth is that you use all three of these modes of heat transfer every day of your life. As a matter of fact, you are a heat transfer expert without knowing it!

To prove it, let's take a common situation, and by analyzing it we will discover how those modes of heat transfer are being utilized instinctively.

Let's suppose that you have been playing tennis on a sunny, hot day. You have become heated up, so you want to cool down. To do it, you take a drink with ice cubes, sit down in the shade of a tree, and start fanning yourself with your tennis hat. You sure feel cooler very soon. Why?

1) You remove yourself from exposure from the warmer source of <u>radiation heat</u> (the sun).

2) You put ice cubes in your drink, so that heat will go from the warm drink to the ice by <u>conduction</u>.

3) You fan yourself with the hat, moving air which will remove heat from your body by <u>convection</u>.

This simple example may serve as a first intuitive notion of these three forms of transmission of heat. All three actually play an extremely important role in the flow of heat into and out of a house, so let's take a closer look.

12

Radiation

or   **The Hot Horseshoe**

FOR SOME REASON which is hard to comprehend, radiation is generally mentioned last in just about every description of transmission of heat. Maybe this is an indication of the importance given until now to radiation in a home situation, because unfortunately, it has been the one most neglected. A clear understanding of how radiation works is essential to the realization of why conventional home cooling techniques are so ineffective and why the new method that we will describe later is so effective. For this reason, let's consider radiation first.

To illustrate how radiation works, let's take a very simple case: pretend you are heating a piece of metal. A horseshoe makes a good example. This horseshoe is made out of atoms of iron which are in constant vibratory motion. This motion generates waves which are radiated in all directions. We don't see those waves simply because they are of very low energy.

Now suppose that we take this horseshoe and start heating it up; for example, on the kitchen stove. If we remove the horseshoe from the stove with a pair of pliers and approach a hand near it, we will feel heat coming out of the piece of metal. What happens here is that the atoms of iron in the horseshoe have now a higher level of energy. They can therefore radiate waves of higher energy; strong enough to make us feel a sensation of heat at a certain distance. This also is radiation, and this type of waves are called infrared.

Why infrared? Simply because if we heat that piece of metal at an even higher temperature with an appropriate device, such as a torch, the metal now will emit waves that not only produce a sensation of heat at a distance, but are of an intensity high enough to stimulate our optic nerve. This is why we say that the metal is "red hot." Of course, if we continue heating the piece of metal at even higher temperatures, the tint of the glow will shift from red to a lighter orange color, ("white hot"), until finally the metal will melt. As you know, molten iron has a bright glow. If you have ever been in a foundry, you probably felt heat at a very considerable distance from the metal: this is due to radiation.

From this simple example, you will realize that every single object emits a certain amount of radiation: your car, your chair, your ring, the walls around you, even your own body. These various objects are at relatively low temperatures, so they will give small amounts of radiation. At the other extreme, the sun, which is at an extemely high temperature, emits an enormous amount of radiation.

Now you will remember that we said that heat transmission always involves a warmer and a cooler place. This means, for example, that your chair receives radiated heat from your body. However, the chair in turn needs a mechanism to get rid of that heat, otherwise the temperature of the chair would keep rising indefinitely. The chair therefore, emits radiation to objects surrounding it. Imagine this process repeated many, many times, and you understand why after a while all objects in a room come to the same temperature.

Now, let's take the case of a house. The sun gives an enormous amount of radiation energy in the form of waves, which are absorbed by any opaque object that is in the way. Notice that in order to absorb radiation, the object must be opaque; that is why air is not heated by the radiation of the sun.

A house is opaque to the sun's rays, and therefore will absorb them. Once this has occurred, the heat will be dissipated by the materials making up the house by all three mechanisms of heat transfer: radiation, conduction, and convection. As we will see later, most of the radiation energy from the sun is absorbed by the roof of the house. Now the roof of the house will tend to dissipate that absorbed energy and therefore will re-emit some of those waves back. But the roof has two surfaces and radiation will occur not only from the outer surface but also from the inner surface which is generally the attic (Figure 13).

62

This radiation is what contributes to increasing the temperature of the house: the radiation emitted by the inner surface of the roof will be absorbed by other objects in the attic which in turn will transmit it to the living areas below.

Of course, the rate of transmission of heat can be reduced, as we have seen before, by insulation. However, we should remember that insulation can only slow down the transmission of heat but not eliminate it, and that the transmission of heat will be faster as the difference in temperatures between the warmer place and the cooler place is larger.

This effect of heating the attic space of a gable roof house is due to what is called "surface emissivity," which incorporates all three forms of heat transmission, and is proportional to the surface area exposed. The inner surface of a roof has an area exposed that is much larger than the outer surface simply because the roof rests on the rafters, which become part of the roof for radiation purposes, as shown in Figure 14.

Figure   13

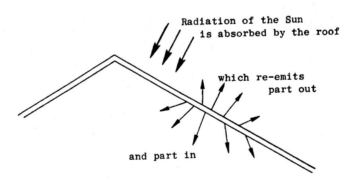

Radiation of the Sun
   is absorbed by the roof

which re-emits
   part out

and part in

Figure 14

THE INTERIOR SURFACE OF THE ROOF IS LARGER THAN THE EXTERIOR SURFACE

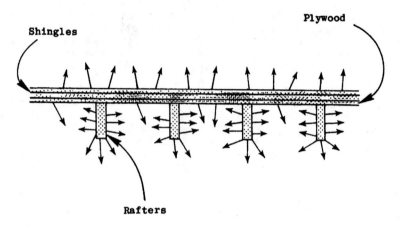

Shingles

Plywood

Rafters

13

Conduction

or   Stuff not moving

I N THE EXAMPLE where a drink was being cooled with ice cubes, heat could pass directly from the liquid to the solid ice even if the drink was not stirred. This is what characterizes heat transmission by conduction: the materials gaining or losing heat do not move. Only the heat does. The most typical case of heat transmission by conduction is a solid wall which is subjected to different temperatures on both sides.

A typical example of it would be the heat that we feel when touching an automobile engine that has been running for a while: the heat was generated inside by combustion of the fuel, but conduction has brought part of that heat to the outside of the engine.

The rate at which heat is transmitted by conduction depends to a large extent on the nature of the material separating the warmer and cooler places. Metals, for example, are effective in transmitting heat by conduction. This is why metals are utilized in the manufacture of heat exchangers such as automobile radiators and heat sinks commonly used in radio receivers. Other materials such as glass, plastics, and wood are much less effective conductors of heat.

As with the other forms of heat transmission, the rate of heat conduction is also proportional to the difference in the temperatures between the warmer place and the cooler place. This, of course, assuming that the other factors are equal, such as the cross section area and the time being considered. Wood is not a pure material but a network of fibers with many tiny pockets. This porosity can vary considerably according to the type of wood. The more porous wood is, the less heat it will transmit by conduction. This means that a very porous wood will be a good insulating material. This is true: balsa wood is used as insulation in some very low-temperature applications, such as tanks for liquified natural gas.

The transmission of heat by conduction in both liquids and gases is very slow. The problem in this case is that usually heat transmission is helped by convection, since both liquids and gases are free to move. One way to prevent this convective movement of liquids or gases is to confine them in extremely small separate compartments. This is, in essence, the principle used in most methods of insulation as the example of balsa wood. Most insulating materials are very light, that is, they are of very low density. Common examples are polystyrene and polyurethane foam and even fiberglass. The way these materials work as insulators is simply by limiting or reducing the convection of air. Therefore, the only way that heat can be transmitted through such materials is by conduction. As we have indicated, conduction is very slow in gases such as air.

From the viewpoint of heat transmission in a house, the most important case of heat transmission by conduction is that of the roof materials. They are in contact with the warm source of highest temperature, that is, the shingles.

When the shingles get warmed by absorption of solar radiation, the heat will be passed by conduction to the layers immediately adjacent to the shingles: roofing paper, plywood, and rafters. The fact that heat is transmitted by conduction to all of these materials can be proven very easily simply by touching the rafters on a very hot day. Sometimes they are frighteningly hot.

Of course, exactly the same mechanism occurs on the outside walls of the house. However, the amount of heat transmitted through the walls is much smaller.

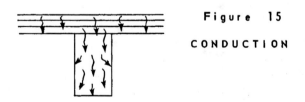

Figure 15

CONDUCTION

14

Convection

or   **Stuff moving**

SOME PEOPLE find it hard to understand heat transmission by radiation or conduction; maybe the reason is that generally one does not <u>see</u> anything happening, except in extreme cases, such as the red hot horseshoe.

Convection, on the other hand, is the form of heat transmission most readily visualized because it involves <u>moving</u> things. This probably explains why convection is usually the mode of heat transfer most widely discussed. It also may be an unconscious reason why it is used so commonly, when other modes would work just as well, often more effectively.

In the tennis example that we described, convection was obtained by fanning air with the hat. You can think of an almost infinite number of similar situations. The closest, of course, is that of the regular electric fan, which produces movement of air, thereby removing heat from a person's body. Other examples are the heating of buildings by hot air, hot water or steam, and even air conditioning itself since it involves the forced movement of cooled air.

All the examples given so far involve the movement of air under *forced* conditions. Convection, however, may also proceed under natural forces. For example, it is an every day observation that when water boils, a pattern of convection such as shown in Figure 16 is developed.

67

Specifically in the case of a house, the most important type of convection heat transfer can be seen in Figure 17. This represents a cross-section of a gable roof, where the heat absorbed from solar radiation sets in motion currents of air surrounding the house following the patterns shown by the arrows. Inside of the roof, that is, in the attic, convection also occurs as shown by the closed loops. The inner surface of the roof acts as the heating element and the air keeps circulating, transferring heat to the attic floor (ceiling of the upper living area) as long as there is a supply of heat through the roof.

Convection is a relatively inefficient form of heat transfer, but, as with the other modes, the rate will increase as the difference in temperature between the warmer place and the cooler place increases. This is certainly so in the case of a hot roof in the summer.

One reason why convection is widely used is that a rapid change of temperature may be obtained if the fluid (liquid or gas) is moved vigorously enough. The trouble is that moving fluids is itself a process that requires considerable amounts of energy. Moving air in an air-heated house requires a good-sized fan. Moving air in an attic, through an attic fan, also requires a powerful motor. An additional problem of the attic fan is that the forced convection that it creates from one end of the house to the other combines with the natural convection shown in Figure 17 to create the spiral pattern (Figure 18), effectively improving the contact between air, the inside surface of the roof, and the floor of the attic. The result is *more* heat transferred, not less. Of course, as the superheated air is expelled from one end, more outside air at lower temperature comes in; so that, overall, there is some cooling effect. However, this small help does not come cheap, as we will see later.

Figure   16

CONVECTION

Figure 17

CONVECTION PATTERNS GENERATED

BY A HOT ROOF

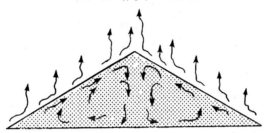

Figure 18

SPIRAL CONVECTION PATTERN

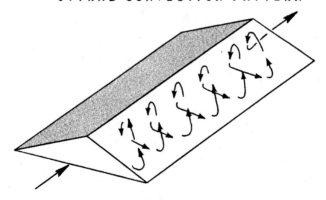

69

Utilities may shut off

your air con~'

During hot summe~
in the near fu+~
may find +'
cond+~

Disaster predicted
by T V A chief

the
~r ~cted
~aces

The
natj
cr

Striking coal miners
ignore back-to-work order

Power conservation urged

Public Utilities Commission
OK's electric rate hike

15

Color

	or	Color it Cool

OUR MINI-EXCURSION through the paths of science will take us now to the fascinating world of color.

Color?? I can imagine many readers saying at this point "But I thought that this book was about home cooling!" It sure is, and by the time you have finished reading this section, you will be in a much better position to understand the extremely important relation between temperature and color.

Color is such a basic human perception that we may sometimes overlook the fact that in order to see color, we must first have light. If there is no light, there is no color: in absolute darkness, we see black. Therefore, perfect black is the absence of any color.

In daylight, we see all colors. Some objects are perfectly white: an example is snow. But we know from the rainbow and from the traditional prism experiment that daylight is composed of many colors. So when daylight hits an object that does not reflect all the light it receives, we will perceive that object as being of a certain color. Different objects act very differently on the light that they receive. This is what gives the world such a magnificent array of tones, shades, and hues.

Have you ever seen snow at night around a house that has only red Christmas light decorations? The snow, of course, appears red. If the next house had only green light decorations, of course the snow would look green. This happens because snow can only reflect the light that it receives. Again, if the light is white, like during the daytime, the snow looks its good old regular white. So we have made a very important finding: that white is white because it reflects <u>all</u> colors of light. If instead of snow we would make the experiment with a chunk of charcoal, we would find that it looks black under <u>all</u> lights. If so, why is a green leaf green under daylight? The answer is simply that the leaf <u>reflects only the green elements</u> in the white light <u>while it absorbs the rest</u>. The same happens with the feathers of a cardinal: it reflects the red elements in the white light while it absorbs all the others.

Now, after talking about such pleasant things as Christmas lights, birds, and leaves, it may sound a bit cruel to say this, but the truth is all of those beautiful colors are forms of <u>electromagnetic radiation</u>. Sorry about that.

That's right. Colors, that is, colored light, are simply components of the visible spectrum, which are rays of a certain wavelength that stimulate the eye. But the visible spectrum is only a small fraction of an enormous range of similar rays having wavelengths varying from much shorter to much longer than the visible waves. The energy of those rays is inversely proportional to their wavelength: rays of long wavelength have low energy, and rays of short wavelength have high energy.

"But"-you may say-"other than for light, what is the use of that electromagnetic radiation stuff?" Well, I bet you use it every day as you drive your car to work. It is called <u>radio</u>. Radio waves are electromagnetic rays of a very long wavelength; so long that your eye does not see them. But your antenna does.

I bet you use electromagnetic radiation every time you make yourself a toast. Because the principal reason why the bread gets toasted is not the convection heat (just try to make a toast in the oven, which is a convection heater) but because of the <u>infrared rays</u>. The reddish glow that you see in the toaster is simply due to the fact that the infrared elements generate a range of wavelengths that include some red light. (You will recall the horseshoe example in the section on Radiation.)

We could keep citing examples of everyday uses of electromagnetic radiation: the X-Ray that they took at your last checkup; the ultraviolet lamp that you hang over your indoor plants; the radar used by the airplane on your last trip; your favorite TV program, etc., etc.

But the purpose of this section is simply to demonstrate that:

- Light is energy.

- Something white <u>reflects all</u> colors of light (all wavelengths of energy).

- Something colored <u>reflects some</u> kinds of light and absorbs some others.

- Something black <u>absorbs all</u> colors of light.

And what happens when something absorbs energy? It gets hot! The darker that something is, the hotter it gets.

Now you start to see the effect of color on the way your house gets hot in the summer. Let's begin with the roof. The shingles are made of black asphalt, an almost perfect energy absorber. True, many shingles have imbedded colored granules, which impart some tonality to the roof for a more pleasing appearance. But since asphalt is the binder, and the granules cannot cover completely the surface, some asphalt is always exposed between the granules. Furthermore, weathering invariably works loose some percentage of the granules, exposing more and more asphalt as the roof ages. Inspect your gutters and you will see there the granules washed off by the rain.

But the energy reflection of shingles with granules of light colors is appreciable enough so as to make a measurable difference. In an experiment to demonstrate that effect, calibrated thermometers were taped to the back of unused roofing shingles and exposed to the sun on a day when the temperature in the shade was 90°F. The results, shown in Figure 19, clearly point out that using the white granuled shingle should result in less heat being transmitted to the plywood, rafters, attic, and eventually, to the living area.

Of course, all of these considerations regarding absorption of radiation and light apply also to the sides of the house, although to a lesser extent, for reasons that we will see in the following section. But the basic rule still holds true: a house painted with a dark color (Barn Red, for example, which is quite common) will absorb much more heat than one painted white or a very light pastel.

An even more unfavorable situation occurs when window

73

shades or draperies are of dark colors. In this case, the sunlight passes through the window panes unaffected, and becomes absorbed and transformed into heat inside of the room. Convection will carry that heat to other parts of the house.

Figure   19

TEMPERATURE RISE IN SHINGLES

OF   DIFFERENT COLORS

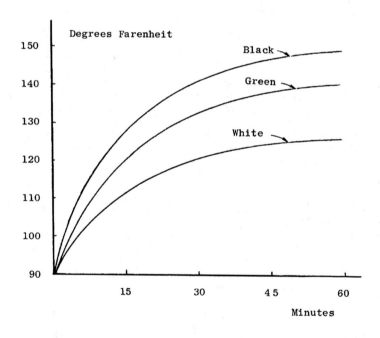

16

Solar Energy

or   How your House gets a Sunburn

THE SEARCH for alternate sources of energy triggered by the shortages of fossil fuels in recent years has made "Solar Energy" a household expression. This is why when one speaks of solar energy, chances are people think only of the "good" aspect of solar fallout, and may bring to mind only the sun collectors of the hot water system that they installed in the house next block. Solar energy, harnessed and converted into useful forms, is already demonstrating great potential for numerous low-temperature applications.

Since, for that reason, people have become more solar-energy-conscious, it is amazing how little attention is being given to the "bad" part of solar fallout. In our case, in which we are considering better ways to cool a home, the bad part may be put, in a simplified manner, this way:

YOUR HOME IS A SUN COLLECTOR.

So let's take a closer look at this inexhaustible source of energy.

The overuse or misuse of the words sun belt and snow belt has gradually led many people to believe that a sunny situation is an almost exclusive property of the southern states. Nothing is farther from the truth. Figure 20 shows the average number of sunshine hours per year across the contiguous 48 states. This map yields the most unexpected surprises. Who would imagine that the southern portion of New York State has about as many hours of

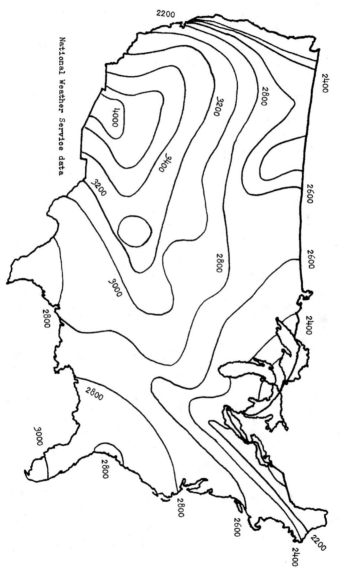

Figure 20

AVERAGE NUMBER OF SUNSHINE HOURS PER YEAR

National Weather Service data

sunshine per year as the state of Louisiana? And you think that Texas is sunny, right? Well, you can watch the sun for about the same amount of time a year in parts of South Dakota.

Of course, latitude has an effect on the amount of energy received by a given area. The reason is that the amount absorbed is influenced somewhat by the angle of incidence: the closer the sun is to the vertical of a place, the more energy will fall on it. Northern states receive sun rays at lower angles of incidence than the southern states, so the amount of solar energy received is lower, other factors being the same.

Yet, the amount of solar flux received is quite substantial, even in a northern location. Table 5 is a compilation of solar fallout data obtained by the U.S. Weather Bureau for a number of cities. Here there are some startling figures.

For example, we can find in Table 5 that the amount of solar energy received by one square foot of area in Boston in June is about 1900 BTU per day. This is over 60 percent of the energy received by "Sun City", Tucson, Arizona. If this does not shake you a bit, let us translate it into more practical terms: at the indicated rate, the energy fallout on the surface area occupied by an average house in the Boston area is roughly equivalent to the heat generated by burning 20 gallons of fuel oil every day. This figure is for the horizontal surface only; the actual figures may be higher because the walls also act as sun collectors, although to a lesser extent.

More significant than yearly figures are the values for the summer months, since these are the important ones for air conditioning. Figure 21, for example shows that virtually the whole country receives over two-thirds of the possible sunshine during the critical months of June to August.

What happens to that massive amount of energy? It will depend on the factors that we discussed before: part of it will be absorbed and transformed into heat, which will be transmitted into the house and then will be pumped back out of the house by an inefficient air conditioner. Just how much energy will follow this path will depend not only on the colors of the house and on the degree to which the house is insulated, but also on the *orientation* of the house. Here also, absorption of energy from a radiant source varies according to the angle of incidence as we have seen above regarding the effect of latitude. Therefore, the orientation of the house and the slope of the roof, will affect energy takeup. Walls receive less energy than the roof because of the high angle of incidence.

77

A house will be in a much more favorable condition to be cooled if it is surrounded by tall trees, because of the shade they will provide. However, it is very unlikely that the shade will be complete and that it will be uniform throughout the day. Even so, a house in the shade of a tree is subject to energy takeup from *scattered* radiation, which is caused by diffusion of the sun's rays, by the atmosphere, by dust, clouds, and even the ground and surrounding structures. This is the same reason why you can get a sunburn at the beach even sitting under an umbrella.

In short, solar energy is a substantial source of the heat in a house practically everywhere in the country. The reason why conventional energy-saving techniques have been so ineffective is that they have practically disregarded this fact.

Figure 21

PERCENTAGE OF POSSIBLE SUNSHINE
(JUNE - AUGUST)

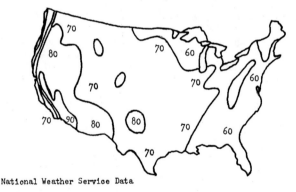

National Weather Service Data

TABLE 5

DAILY AVERAGES OF SOLAR ENERGY RECEIVED ON A HORIZONTAL SURFACE

BTU/FT^2 DAY

	JAN	FEB	MAR	APR	MAY	JUN	JUL	AUG	SEP	OCT	NOV	DEC
Alburquerque, NM	1133	1345	1834	2236	2494	2749	2502	2299	2018	1712	1284	1085
Boston, MA	601	923	1196	1465	1758	1911	1838	1708	1343	1077	601	498
Charleston, SC	923	1232	1664	2059	2288	2166	1989	1945	1509	1203	1137	786
Lincoln, NB	686	930	1247	1576	1852	2052	2122	1775	1509	1114	771	613
New York, NY	450	705	956	1339	1572	1646	1620	1351	1166	897	546	395
Oak Ridge, TN	642	852	1055	1483	2103	2000	1838	1708	1517	1129	753	598
St. Cloud, MN	627	878	1461	1734	2070	2066	2118	1667	1343	1048	646	561
Salt Lake City, UT	572	908	1424	1882	2015	2192	2303	2247	1631	1026	661	442
Spokane, WA	443	731	1240	2111	1782	2269	2487	2144	1587	923	491	280
Tucson, AZ	1161	1442	1991	2415	2688	2577	2308	2168	2102	1630	1313	1124

17

Sensible vs. Latent Heat

or   What you can't feel can help you

WE HAVE REFERRED ALREADY on a number of occasions to objects that are cold and to objects that are hot. Heat and cold are terms with which we are familiar since our earliest age. We know that something is hot or cold by merely touching the object. That is why this type of heat is called <u>sensible</u> heat: because it can be sensed, felt.

There is another type of heat which we use every day in our lives, that is not nearly as obvious to many of us. It is called <u>latent</u> heat. What is latent heat? Maybe the answer can be given most easily with an example. In fact, let's continue with the example of cooling after a tennis game, with a drink and ice cubes. Why does the drink get cold? Most people believe that the only reason why ice cools is that it is cold. This is partially true: ice must have a temperature of 32°F or lower. However, if we would count on the sensible heat of ice as the only source of cooling, our drink would not get very cold, and moreover, the cooling effect would not last very long. The heat would pass from the drink to the ice, and soon the mixture would be at the same temperature.

But the real reason why ice cools a drink so well is that *ice melts into water* and this is a change that consumes a lot of heat. In other words, most of the heat absorbed by the ice in cooling a liquid is not used to warm up the ice, but to turn the ice into water. This heat, in the case of a solid that turns into a liquid, is called latent heat of fusion. Latent, because you

81

can not feel it, but it is there, waiting to be used.

There are many similar examples. Solids turn into liquids, and liquids into vapors; these are called changes of state. To produce changes between these three forms, large amounts of heat must be supplied or removed. The heat needed to change a liquid into a gas is called latent heat of evaporation. This is another form of latent heat which we have used perhaps since we were children. When you were small and had a high fever, your mother probably gave you an alcohol rub. The purpose of this was simply to cool the body and reduce the fever. The reason for using alcohol is that it evaporates very fast and it has a high value of latent heat of evaporation. When the alcohol evaporates from your skin, it removes heat from your body.

Let's go back again to the example of cooling off after tennis. We said that when fanning yourself with the hat, you cooled by forced convection. This is true; but similarly to the case of the ice in your drink, most of the relief that you felt was not due to the air passing by you, but to the latent heat of evaporation of your sweat.

This is also what happens when you stand in front of a fan. Initially, you feel a strong relief because of the evaporation of surface moisture from your body. However, the fan is very effective, and removes the moisture quickly. This is the reason why after standing in front of the fan for a while, its effectiveness decreases, and in fact may feel uncomfortably warm after a few minutes. There is no more surface water to take up heat.

The latent heat of evaporation of water is used in many industries. For example, water used for refrigeration purposes that has become hot is often cooled again by spraying it on cooling ponds. The larger area exposed favors the loss of heat by rapid evaporation.

Even more efficient are cooling towers, where water is sprayed against an upward-moving stream of forced air, which further hastens water evaporation and therefore a drop in temperature.

In short:

1) WATER EVAPORATES.
2) WHEN WATER EVAPORATES, IT TAKES UP LATENT HEAT.
3) LATENT HEAT CAN THEREFORE BE USED IN COOLING.

18

Atmospheric Humidity

or   **One wet , One dry**

SO WATER EVAPORATES from cooling towers. And from cooling ponds. And from the sweat of people. And from swimming pools, rivers, lakes, oceans... Wait! Can this go on forever? Isn't there a limit to the amount of water that can evaporate?

The answer is yes and no. Water cannot continue to evaporate indefinitely because there is a limit to how much water vapor can exist in a given amount of air at a given temperature. But, on the other hand, periodically atmospheric conditions are such that moisture condenses in the form of rain, thus "making room," so to say, for more water to evaporate. Such is the marvelous dynamic equilibrium in nature. And, since evaporation and rain occur simultaneously somewhere in the world, for all practical purposes the answer to the question is "yes, we can evaporate water almost continuously."

The question, therefore, is not really whether we <u>can</u> evaporate water, but how fast. And here is where the idea of atmospheric humidity comes into play. As the name indicates, humidity is a measure of how much water vapor there is in the air at a given time.

This concentration could be expressed as a weight percentage. The problem is that the maximum amount of water vapor that air can carry varies very rapidly with temperature: the higher the temperature, the more it can carry. So a concentration

83

expressed as a weight percentage at one temperature does not give an accurate idea of the situation at another temperature.

Air that contains the maximum amount of water vapor possible is called *saturated*. So, a convenient way to indicate the existing concentration of water vapor in air is expressing it as a percentage of the amount needed for saturation. And this is the relative humidity. For example, a relative humidity of 25 percent means that the air at that particular time contains 25 percent of the water vapor concentration necessary to saturate it. Since this leaves 75 percent of the air's capacity available, water will evaporate fast under those conditions. If, on the other hand, the existing relative humidity is 98 percent, it means that the air is almost saturated, and the evaporation of water will be slow.

It is simple to find out the relative humidity of air at any given time, with the help of a simple and inexpensive instrument called the psychrometer (Figure 22). The instrument consists simply of two very accurate thermometers mounted on a frame that can spin on a handle. The bulb of one of the thermometers is covered by a fabric sleeve. To make a measurement, the fabric-covered bulb is dipped in water so as to soak well the cloth, and the assembly is whirled vigorously.

Water evaporates from the wet fabric, taking up latent heat of evaporation, so that the temperature of the thermometer drops. Whirling is continued until the temperature of the wet-bulb thermometer does not drop any further. At this point, the two temperatures are recorded, and the relative humidity is found in Table 6.

Figure 22

PSYCHROMETER

Table 6

R E L A T I V E   H U M I D I T Y

DIFFERENCE BETWEEN THE DRY AND WET THERMOMETERS °F

Air Temp	1	2	3	4	5	6	7	8	9	10	11	12	13	14	15	16	17	18	19	20	21	22	23	24	25	26	27	28	29	30	31	32	33	34	35	36	Air Temp
30	89	78	67	56	46	36	26	16	6																												30
35	91	81	72	63	54	45	36	27	19	10	2																										35
40	92	83	75	68	60	52	45	37	29	22	15	7																									40
45	93	86	78	71	64	57	51	44	38	31	25	18	12	6																							45
50	93	87	80	74	67	61	55	49	43	38	32	27	21	16	10	5																					50
55	94	88	82	76	70	65	59	54	49	43	38	33	28	23	19	14	9	5																			55
60	94	89	83	78	73	68	63	58	53	48	44	39	34	30	26	21	17	13	9	5	1																60
65	95	90	85	80	75	70	66	61	56	52	48	44	39	35	31	27	24	20	16	12	9	5	2														65
70	95	90	86	81	77	72	68	64	59	55	51	47	44	40	36	33	30	27	24	20	18	15	12	9	6	3											70
75	96	91	86	82	78	74	70	66	62	58	54	51	47	44	40	37	34	30	27	24	21	18	15	12	10	7	5	3	1								75
80	96	91	87	83	79	75	72	68	64	61	57	54	50	47	44	41	38	35	32	29	26	24	21	18	15	13	11	9	7	5	3	1					80
85	96	92	88	84	80	77	73	70	66	63	60	56	53	50	47	44	41	39	36	33	30	28	25	22	20	17	15	13	11	9	6	4	2				85
90	96	92	89	85	81	78	74	71	68	65	61	58	55	52	49	47	44	42	39	36	34	31	29	26	24	22	19	17	15	13	11	9	7	5	3	1	90
95	96	93	89	86	82	79	76	72	69	66	63	60	56	54	51	49	47	44	42	39	37	35	32	30	28	25	23	21	19	17	15	13	11	10	8	6	95
100	96	93	90	87	83	80	77	73	70	68	65	62	59	56	54	51	49	46	44	41	39	37	35	33	30	28	26	24	22	21	19	17	15	13	12	10	100
105	97	93	90	87	84	81	78	75	72	69	66	64	61	58	56	53	51	49	46	44	42	40	38	35	33	31	30	28	26	24	22	21	19	17	15	14	105
110	97	93	90	87	84	81	78	75	73	70	67	65	62	60	57	55	52	50	48	46	44	42	40	38	36	34	32	30	28	26	25	23	21	20	18	17	110
115	97	94	91	88	85	82	79	76	74	71	69	66	64	61	59	57	54	52	50	48	46	44	43	40	38	36	34	33	31	29	28	26	24	23	21	20	115
120	97	94	91	88	85	82	80	77	74	72	69	67	65	62	60	58	55	53	51	49	47	45	43	41	40	38	36	34	33	31	29	28	26	25	23	22	120
	1	2	3	4	5	6	7	8	9	10	11	12	13	14	15	16	17	18	19	20	21	22	23	24	25	26	27	28	29	30	31	32	33	34	35	36	

Example: Assume a "dry bulb" temperature of 90°F and a "wet bulb" temperature of 80°F. The difference is 10°F. Locate the number 90 in the vertical column marked "Air Temperatures" and the number 10 in the horizontal column marked "Difference". Follow the columns to their intersection and read 65. Relative humidity is 65 %.

PART THREE:

The Solution

19

The Solution is LEC

or   Why not Make the House Sweat , too ?

WHAT IS LEC?

LEC stands for Latent Evaporative Cooling. It is the cooling effect that accompanies the evaporation of a liquid, such as water. We can use LEC to cool homes, the same way we got cool by the evaporation of our sweat after tennis. But you may recall that once the sweat evaporated, even blowing air with a fan did not help in cooling. So to cool a house, we must provide a *continuous* supply of water. Since the roof is the warmest place in a house, from which considerable heat is transmitted inside, the most effective water evaporation will take place if direct contact is provided between water and the roof.

The key point in obtaining efficient evaporation is to produce a <u>thin</u> layer of water on the roof. Fortunately, although there are hundreds of house styles, virtually every home in this country has a sloped roof, either gable, gambrel or straight (Figure 23) which provides by simple gravity flow a natural way of forming a thin layer of water without stationary puddles.

In houses having a flat roof or a mansard roof (Figure 24) it will be more difficult to control the distribution of water. It can be done, although less effectively. We will look into these cases in a later section.

It cannot be emphasized strongly enough that the cooling effect obtained by LEC is due solely to the evaporation of water,

Figure   23

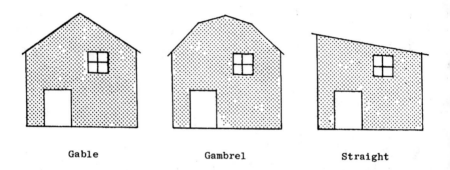

Gable   Gambrel   Straight

and **NOT** to the convection of large amounts of water flowing by. In fact, the method is most effective with thin layers of water.

You cannot control the amount of water evaporating from the roof. That is determined by things such as the size of the roof, its shape, slope, location, orientation, color, and so on. But you *can* control the amount of water that you supply to the roof. The trick is to hit the right balance between the amount of water that evaporates from the roof, and the amount of water supplied to the roof. Too little water will not take full advantage of the cooling potential available, while too much water will cool by convection, actually retarding evaporation. As we have seen, the cooling potential of a change of state is much larger than that of convection. Proper regulation and distribution of water are therefore important factors in getting the most out of the system.

Figure 24

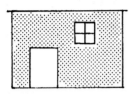

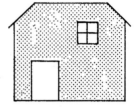

Flat   Mansard

Until now we have talked of Latent Evaporative Cooling in rather general terms; let us look now at some hard numbers.

The amount of heat taken away when water evaporates, that is, the latent heat of evaporation, varies somewhat, from about 1000 to about 1100 BTU/pound, depending on the temperature at which evaporation occurs. This is shown in Figure 25: the higher the temperature, the lower the latent heat of evaporation. In other words, we will need more water to cool a roof which has already been heated up by the sun, than to keep it at the early morning ambient temperature.

However, for our purposes, we will take a value of 1040 BTU/pound as a reasonable average. This value means that every time a pound of water (about two cups) evaporates, it takes with it about 1040 BTUs. These are such impressive numbers, and this relationship is so useful in driving home the value of Latent Evaporative Cooling, that we will repeat them in somewhat more direct words, in capitals, underlined, and boxed:

> **IF TWO CUPS OF WATER EVAPORATE FROM YOUR ROOF,**
>
> **THEY TAKE MORE THAN 1000 BTUs of HEAT AWAY.**

An even more meaningful comparison may be made if we consider that a typical small room air conditioner has a cooling capacity of 5000 BTU. What this rating means is that when operating at full capacity, the air conditoner can remove 5000 BTU every hour. We have seen that when a pound of water evaporates, it takes with it more than 1000 BTUs. So the cooling capacity of our

91

air conditioner could be theoretically replaced with the cooling capacity of about 5 pounds of water. Since one gallon of water weighs 8.33 pounds, 5 pounds are 0.6 gallons or slightly more than a half gallon. That is,

WHEN ABOUT A HALF GALLON OF WATER EVAPORATES,

IT REMOVES AN AMOUNT OF HEAT ROUGHLY EQUIVALENT

TO THAT REMOVED BY A 5,000 BTU AIR CONDITIONER

IN ONE HOUR.

By now surely there are some rates, costs, and miscellaneous numbers bouncing around in your head. Good. You have started to get a rough idea of the economic potential of such equivalence. We will make a more accurate cost comparison in a later section.

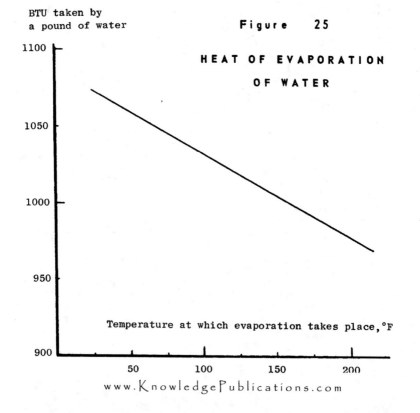

BTU taken by a pound of water

Figure   25

HEAT OF EVAPORATION

OF WATER

Temperature at which evaporation takes place, °F

20

Distribution

A KEY FACTOR to obtain efficient heat transfer from the roof to the water and subsequent evaporation is to provide a means for the liquid to form a thin film over most of the roof area. This is the function of the distribution system, which spreads the water that has been carried to the roof by some appropriate means (Figure 26).

The most economical, although temporary way to carry water to the roof is simply by using a garden hose from the closest faucet on the exterior of the house.

The hose should be attached to the house at certain intervals, to avoid damage by its weight once full. Use wide clamps and be sure not to pinch the hose. Of course, a more permanent and expensive setup can be made with pipes. Rigid PVC pipe is adequate for this purpose. All installations should conform to the local codes. If you install a permanent line, include a bleed-off drain spigot at the lowest point to facilitate emptying it when the cooling season is over. At the edge of the roof, the carrier hose or pipe connect through an elbow to the distributing section.

Since the purpose of the distribution system is to obtain uniform coverage by a thin film of water, the best bet is to provide some form of spraying. This can be accomplished in various ways:

93

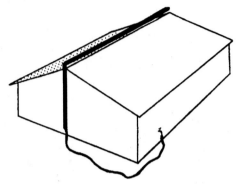

Figure   26

DISTRIBUTION

     1) Punctured Hose: An effective and economical method (although not permanent) is to place on the roof a hose that has many punctures, so that water produces fine squirts that break into droplets.   This type of hose is used frequently to water newly-seeded lawns, because they have requirements quite similar to those in our application: a continuous supply of small amounts of water uniformly distributed over a large area.   Depending on the local conditions, such as height of the house, water pressure, shape and dimensions of the roof, etc., you should be able to figure out whether to use one or more hoses, round or flat, etc.   Figure 27 presents suggested layouts.

     2) Sprinkler Type: The main distributing pipe branches out through T's to both sides of the roof, and spray heads are positioned so that the spray covers most of the roof (Figure 28). The section of the main pipe should be of progressively smaller diameter downstream, to compensate for pressure drop.

Figure   27

HOSE   SYSTEMS

3) Oscillating Sprinkler: This is another variety of watering gizmo used on lawns (Figure 29). An advantage of this device is that it covers a rectangular pattern, so that just one sprinkler will take care of the whole roof. Usually the product label indicates the size of the area covered, so that the proper model for the house may be purchased.

This type of sprinkler, however, has the disadvantage that it provides a somewhat coarse spray, so that it is not very efficient. One way to solve this problem is to plug the existing holes with epoxy or silicone putty, then drill holes of a smaller diameter. In addition, the sprinkler must be positioned across the apex line of the roof, which may require constructing a saddle to set and secure it properly (Figure 30).

Figure 28

PIPE SYSTEM

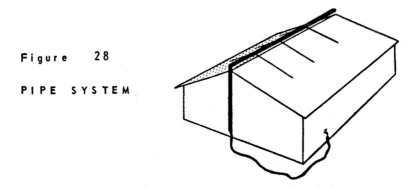

If the area covered by the sprinkler is larger than the house, closing the water faucet half-way will reduce the pressure and therefore the reach of the sprinkler. If you live in an area that has steady winds coming from a given direction, these will shift the spray pattern somewhat; change the distribution system to compensate and check again. Remember that the breeze is not perfectly steady, so that it will shift the water spray periodically, enough to wet areas beyond and around the main spray pattern.

Whatever the type of distributing system you chose, trial and error will show the best positoning for maximum efficiency. Do not attempt to spray every square inch of the roof. This will result in waste.

A fine spray is desirable not only because of uniform distribution and economic operation, but also because the water itself will become slightly cooler. As it travels its trajactory from the distributing device to the roof surface, some water evaporates from the droplets, lowering their temperature, and thus, providing additional cooling power.

Since the surface of the shingles is rough, and, in addition, there are numerous edges, the water will tend to form little "rivers" downstream near the gutters rather than come down as a uniform, continuous film. Don't fret about this, as it will not affect substantially the performance of the system.

Take time and experiment with your distribution system: it will pay as a more efficient operation.

Figure 29

OSCILLATING SPRINKLER

Figure 30

SADDLE

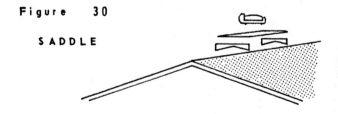

21

Regulation

or   Just Enough

THE ECONOMICAL OPERATION of the Latent Evaporative Cooling system requires supplying the roof with as much water as that surface can evaporate, but no more. If the amount of water supplied is insufficient, the full cooling potential of the roof will not be utilized. If, on the other hand, more than the evaporative capacity is supplied, excess water will be wasted down the gutter leaders. Even worse, a large excess of water will actually slow down the evaporative process.

Both extremes may be avoided by regulating the flow of water through an appropriate device. The most basic, of course, is the faucet to which the supply hose is attached. Regulation is, therefore, manual. Open the faucet enough so as to get the distributing section operating correctly: some spray devices will not operate properly below a certain minimum volume of liquid. Check the pattern for completeness of coverage. If you use more than one hose or spray head, make sure that the areas covered by adjacent sprinklers do not overlap. If necessary, shut off the water, reposition the sprinklers and check again. The ideal situation is attained when there is a <u>slight</u> dripping on the gutters, indicating that the evaporative capacity of the roof has just been exceeded. Put pails at the gutter spouts so as to collect the excess; you can use this to water your garden. You should be able to adjust to a satisfactory operation in a few times, after which the system can be left on its own.

Do not leave the system running when the house is not

supervised, even for a few hours: a hose may burst, for example, and considerable amounts of water may be wasted. If you must leave the house regularly during the hours of operation, you may want to install a timer, such as those used in underground lawn sprinkler systems.

The best way to regulate the flow, of course, is to open the water only when the roof is hot, and close it when the roof has cooled enough. This can be done automatically with a self-contained temperature-control valve. There are many types of control valves that will do this job, but all have several features in common: 1) a closing device (ball, gate, or butterfly), 2) an actuator, which can be pneumatic, but in a home situation it is better if it is electric, and 3) a temperature sensing and switching device. The sensor can be installed in a remote location (the inside surface of the roof, in our case). The switching device can be set so that when the temperature of the roof reaches a certain point, the actuator opens the water valve. When enough water has been sprayed, and the temperature of the roof has come down to a preset level, the actuator shuts off the water valve. These valves are of course not inexpensive, but over the years they will more than save their cost.

Following are the names and addresses of some manufacturers of control valves.

Leonard Valve Co.
1360 Elmwood Avenue
Cranston, Rhode Island 02910

Continental Hydraulics
Savape, Minnesota 55378

Barker-Colman Co.
1300 Rock Street
Rockford, Illinois 61101

OEM Controls, Inc.
1 Bishop Street
Norwalk, Connecticut 06851

Texcentric, Inc.
P.O. Box 19312 TR
Houston, Texas 77024

Barksdale Controls Co.
Alcoa & Fruitland Road
Los Angeles, California 90058

Jordon Valve Co.
407 Blade Street
Cincinnati, Ohio 45216

Backman Valve Corp.
1110 Volunteer Parkway
Bristol, Tennessee 37620

22

Cost

or   There is a Water Meter ,too

UNLESS YOU ARE one of those lucky homeowners that has his own water well, you are now thinking of your water bill.

It is very difficult to estimate the amount of water needed to run your LEC system, because there are so many individual factors involved: geographic location, house size, type of sprinkler, and percentage of time used, to name a few.

Just as in the case of the rate schedules for electricity, water utilities charge on a sliding scale; that is, the more you use, the lower the price per cubic foot. Therefore, rates can be compared only at similar usage volume levels.

The following cost figures in Table 7 were compiled from a study of 1976 monthly water rates, authored by D. L. Chambers, of the Water Bureau of the Metropolitan District, Hartford, Connecticut, for a level of 10,000 cubic feet. The numbers in the second column are the calculated cost per cubic foot at that usage volume. Copies of the full report are available from the Americal Water Works Association, 6666 W. Quincy Avenue, Denver, Colorado 80235.

TABLE 7

RESIDENTIAL RATES FOR WATER SERVICE IN VARIOUS CITIES

City	$/10,000 cubic feet	Cents per cubic foot
Akron, Ohio	45.15	0.4515
Amarillo, Texas	26.86	0.2686
Austin, Texas	39.84	0.3984
Baltimore, Maryland	24.33	0.2433
Birmingham, Alabama	47.00	0.4700
Boston, Massachusetts	47.22	0.4722
Bridgeport, Connecticut	60.02	0.6002
Charlotte, North Carolina	42.11	0.4211
Cleveland, Ohio	14.53	0.1453
Clifton, New Jersey	23.20	0.2320
Columbus, Ohio	39.70	0.3970
Dayton, Ohio	26.40	0.2640
Dearborn, Michigan	24.54	0.2454
Denver, Colorado	33.45	0.3345
Des Moines, Iowa	39.80	0.3980
El Paso, Texas	25.14	0.2514
Grand Rapids, Michigan	18.00	0.1800
Guilford, Connecticut	51.87	0.5187
Hartford, Connecticut	53.80	0.5380
Honolulu, Hawaii	20.25	0.2025
Indianapolis, Indiana	59.85	0.5985
Jackson, Mississippi	35.40	0.3540
Jacksonville, Florida	39.50	0.3950
Kansas City, Missouri	33.00	0.3300
Little Rock, Arkansas	43.06	0.4306
Long Beach, California	29.30	0.2930
Lubbock, Texas	32.25	0.3225
Madison, Wisconsin	16.50	0.1650
Miami, Florida	29.73	0.2973
Milwaukee, Wisconsin	28.07	0.2807

City	$/10,000 cubic feet	Cents per cubic foot
New Britain, Connecticut	37.25	0.3725
New London, Connecticut	56.25	0.5625
New Orleans, Louisiana	21.05	0.2105
Oakland, California	22.80	0.2280
Omaha, Nebraska	33.40	0.3340
Peoria Heights, Illinois	56.07	0.5607
Phoenix, Arizona	23.00	0.2300
Pittsbugh, Pennsylvania	54.75	0.5475
Portland, Maine	29.28	0.2928
Providence, Rhode Island	19.31	0.1931
Raleigh, North Carolina	53.71	0.5371
Richmond, Virginia	30.45	0.3045
Rochester, New York	53.42	0.5342
Rockford, Illinois	26.77	0.2677
Sacramento, California	18.00	0.1800
Saint Louis, Missouri	28.24	0.2824
Saint Paul, Minnesota	38.00	0.3800
Saint Petersburg, Florida	50.91	0.5091
Salt Lake City, Utah	16.00	0.1600
San Antonio, Texas	35.70	0.3570
San Diego, California	34.30	0.3430
San Francisco, California	29.87	0.2987
San Jose, California	36.90	0.3690
Savannah, Georgia	34.83	0.3483
Seattle, Washington	22.76	0.2276
Shreveport, Louisiana	39.00	0.3900
South Bend, Indiana	25.55	0.2555
Springfield, Massachusetts	2517	0.2517
Stockton, California	18.00	0.1800
Tacoma, Washington	15.60	0.1560
Tampa, Florida	36.00	0.3600
Topeka, Kansas	47.50	0.4750
Waterbury, Connecticut	32.60	0.3260
Wichita, Kansas	30.22	0.3022
Worcester, Massachusetts	29.17	0.2917
Yonkers, New York	50.66	0.5066

101

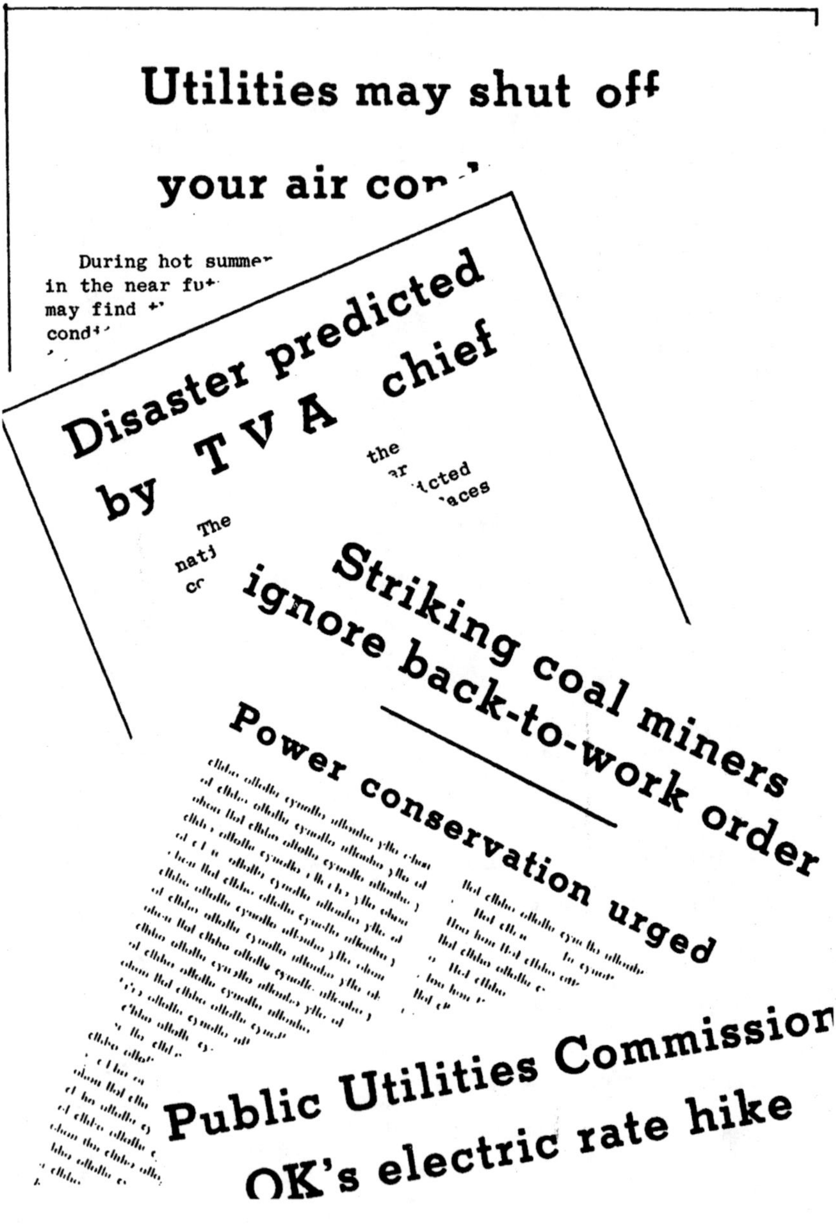
Utilities may shut off
your air con
During hot summer
in the near fu
may find
cond
Disaster predicted
by T V A chief
the
dicted
aces
The
nat
Striking coal miners
ignore back-to-work order
Power conservation urged
Public Utilities Commission
OK's electric rate hike

23

The Attic Fan

or   How to Bake Antiques

HAVE YOU EVER HAD to climb to your attic on a summer day to hunt for the trunk that your kid needed for camp? How about to scavenge oldies for the flea market? If you are like me, you came down sweaty, dusty, and grouchy, and headed right for the shower. Yes, the attic can get hot.

It has been recognized for a long time that temperature buildup in the attic is responsible for a substantial portion of the heat that reaches the living levels of a house. This is why many attempts have been made to eliminate it by venting the heated air to the outside, replacing it with air at the prevailing ambient temperature.

Warmer air is lighter than cooler air, and thus it tends to rise. This causes the convection currents that we discussed in Section 13. A natural way to eliminate warmer air, therefore, is to provide a clear passage to the outside at or near the highest point of the roof, where natural draft (Figure 31) or turbine type (Figure 32) vents may be installed. This method of natural convection provides some measure of relief.

But more and more common is the forced-convection method, which provides faster air movement through the use of an electric fan. This may be placed horizontally between the attic and the living space immediately below, vertically at an opening in an end wall, roof-mounted, or in a combination of these ways.

Figure 31

NATURAL DRAFT VENT

Although far from being the answer to our problems, this attic fan does help, to the extent that it produces a measurable advantage. It is just unfortunate that some people are so conditioned to pay exorbitant air conditioning bills, that the small improvement provided by the attic fan is generally overrated. Also, many people think that it is a "free" way to save energy.

Very often attic fans are advertised as being capable of "reducing your air conditioning bill by 1/3" (or more in some cases). In the next section we will see that in a typical situation, the target savings for a fan is considerably less than that.

Regarding the belief that the attic fan provides a "free" way to save energy, let us consider some figures. A typical fan costs about $150. Installation may run another $50, for a total of $200. If we assume that the useful life of the fan is 10 years, your depreciation cost is about $20 a year, or about $5 per seasonal month. But now we have to *operate* the fan. And that is a problem, because moving large masses of air requires quite a bit of power. Typical 22 to 24 inch fans for the 40 feet house that we discussed before are powered by motors rated at about 6 amps. Electric consumption, therefore, is 6 amp x 120 volts = 720 watt. Running it for 10 hours a day, it consumes close to 7200 watts hour. If your electric rate is about 6¢/kWh, the daily cost to run it is about $0.43, or $12.90 a month. Add the $5 depreciation, and it comes to about $18 a month. Still a good buy, but don't think it is free!

104

You will remember from the sections on Transmission of Heat, that the air in the attic gets heated by convection flow near the hot inside surface of the roof, rafters, etc. That is, in order for the attic fan to do the job it is supposed to do, the roof MUST be hot.

IF THE ROOF IS NOT HOT, THE AIR DOES NOT GET HEATED.
IF THE AIR DOES NOT GET HEATED, THERE IS NO POINT IN
HAVING AN ATTIC FAN.

If the roof is hot, there is radiation, which the air cannot stop. Since air is a poor conductor of heat, its effect in removing heat from the roof is slow. Increasing the size of the fan beyond a certain point, therefore, will not help much. And, furthermore, remember that the attic fan has a basic limitation: you can put a fan big enough to blow the house away, but it cannot cool the attic one bit below the outside temperature.

LEC can, for the same reason that the wet-bulb thermometer can show a lower temperature than the dry one.

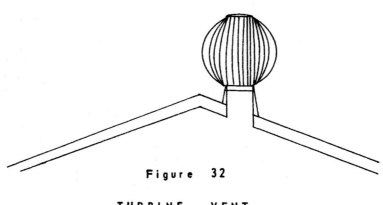

Figure   32

TURBINE   VENT

24

Test House

or   Proof of the Pudding

THE VALUE OF LATENT EVAPORATIVE COOLING has been demonstrated in actual tests run under rigidly controlled conditions in a house in the metropolitan New York-New Jersey area. The temperature was checked in various places of the house and the usage of utilities was monitored closely, with several different combinations of equipment. This section presents in detail how the test was performed, the data collected, and calculations made with them.

Tests of this nature are extremely difficult to run for one simple reason: no two days ever have identical weather conditions. Data collected on a sunny day cannot be compared to that of a cloudy day. Different wind conditions change results. The only way to avoid this problem is to run simulated tests on a laboratory scale. Even so, laboratory results are never totally accepted unless they have been confirmed in a real use environment. So we go back to the issue of weather variability.

One way to overcome the problem is to run tests for several years. That way, variations in one direction hopefully will be compensated by similar variations in the other direction over a sufficiently long period of time. This is a statistical method, similar to the one we used to calculate the usage of electricity for air conditioning in Section 8. Running tests for several years is difficult and expensive.

Another way is to hit a string of days having weather

so similar that it may be considered equal for all practical purposes. The trouble with this method is that, of course, one does not know if the weather will remain constant for a period of time, until the period is over. The way to use this method, therefore, is to test, test, and keep testing until one is lucky with a given number of days. This period should not extend for over one week, because factors such as location of the sun's trajectory in the sky and duration of daylight may start changing enough to make a difference.

One such lucky string of days occurred during July of 1977. A stationary heat wave covered almost the whole country, prompting newspapers to call the month "the worst July since the Dust Bowl." Heat was front-page news everywhere.

Thanks to the stationary nature of the weather pattern, the temperature, humidity, wind, barometric pressure, and sunshine were almost constant during July 16th through 21st, as shown in the tables compiled by the National Weather Service.

The test was performed on a 15-year-old frame bi-level house of approximately 43 x 25 feet, with the front of the house facing due North. There are no trees tall enough to give shade to the roof.

The roof is gable, 12 percent pitch, extending beyond the wall to provide a 2-feet eave on the north side only. The shingles are of a pastel color, and given the age, they have lost some of the colored granules. The gabled roof provides a crawl attic space over the entire surface of the house. There are windows on the walls at both ends of the attic. There is an attic fan rated at 2000 cubic feet/minute, which is in accordance to standards for the volume involved. It is mounted on the window in the wall facing East, since prevailing winds come from the West. The window facing West provides the area for air intake as required.

The insulation between the attic and the upper living area consists of the original 3 inch-thick roll-type fiberglass, plus 3 inches of raked-on fiberglass wool, which filled the space between the 2 x 6 joints. Plywood flooring, 1/2 inch thick, was then installed on the center half of the attic, for the entire length of the house. The attic has a considerable amount of usual household items, which provide some additional insulating value.

Air conditioning of the upper living area is obtained with two through-the-wall units, one rated at 18,000 BTU/220 Volts, mounted on the West wall by the living/dining rooms, and one

108

WS Form B-16 NY

U.S. DEPARTMENT OF COMMERCE
NATIONAL OCEANIC AND ATMOSPHERIC ADMINISTRATION
NATIONAL WEATHER SERVICE

SURFACE WEATHER OBSERVATIONS
DAILY RECORD

TABLE 8

STATION NEW YORK, N.Y. Central Park

DATE Saturday, July 16, 1977

TO CONVERT LST TO GMT ADD 5 hrs. SUBTRACT 0 hrs.

TIME (E.S.T.) (1)	TEMPERATURE (°F) (2)	PRECIPITATION (Inches) (3)	WIND DIRECTION (4)	WIND SPEED (M.P.H.) (5)	SUNSHINE (Minutes) (6)	SKY COVER (Scale 0-10) (7)	WEATHER (8)	PEAK GUST 20 MPH OR MORE (M) (9)	RELATIVE HUMIDITY (10)	DEW POINT (11)	T-HI (12)	BEGINNINGS AND ENDINGS OF METEOROLOGICAL PHENOMENA, REMARKS, NOTES, ETC. (13)	SLP (14)	SEA LEVEL PRESSURE (Inches) (14)	TIME (E.S.T.)
00-01	77		SSW	9					62	63	73		200	30.12	00-01
01-02	76		SSW	10					66	64	72			30.12	01-02
02-03	75		SSW	6					66	63	73			30.12	02-03
03-04	75		SSW	8					66	63	73		200	30.12	03-04
04-05	75		SW	8					66	63	73			30.13	04-05
05-06	75		SW	7					66	63	73			30.13	05-06
06-07	76		SW	7					69	65	73		213	30.16	06-07
07-08	79		SW	5					65	66	75			30.16	07-08
08-09	84		SW	6					57	67	77			30.15	08-09
09-10	90		WNW	5					50	69	81		210	30.15	09-10
10-11	92		SSW	2					49	70	82			30.15	10-11
11-12	96		WSW	3					46	72	84			30.15	11-12
12-13	98		NW	4					44	72	85		196	30.11	12-13
13-14	98		NW	5					45	73	86			30.10	13-14
14-15	98		NW	5					44	72	85			30.08	14-15
15-16	96		NW	5					45	71	84		186	30.08	15-16
16-17	92		NW	7					46	68	81			30.09	16-17
17-18	90		NW	6					49	68	81			30.08	17-18
18-19	87	T	NW	7					54	68	80	RB 1801 RE 1812	186	30.08	18-19
19-20	86		SW	6					53	67	78			30.13	19-20
20-21	81		SW	5					63	67	76			30.11	20-21
21-22	81		SSW	4					63	67	76		196	30.11	21-22
22-23	80		NE	8					65	67	76			30.10	22-23
23-24	81		ENE	7					63	67	76			30.09	23-24
SUM				157											
AVER.			PREVAILING SW	6.5	POSS 887										
MISC.					%										

SYMBOLS USED IN COLUMN 8

A—HAIL	IP—ICE PELLETS	DL—DISTANT LIGHTNING
R—RAIN	L—DRIZZLE	ZL—FREEZING DRIZZLE
S—SNOW	T—THUNDERSTORM	ZR—FREEZING RAIN

SURFACE WEATHER OBSERVATIONS
DAILY RECORD

STATION: **NEW YORK, N.Y.** Central Park

DATE: **Monday, July 18, 1977**

TO CONVERT LST TO GMT — ADD 5 hrs. SUBTRACT 0 hrs.

TIME (E.S.T.) (1)	TEMPERATURE (°F) (2)	PRECIPITATION (inches) (3)	WIND DIRECTION (4)	WIND SPEED (M.P.H.) (5)	SUNSHINE (Minutes) (6)	SKY COVER (Scale 0-10) (7)	WEATHER (8)	PEAK GUST 20 MPH OR MORE (9)	RELATIVE HUMIDITY (10)	DEW POINT (11)	T H I (12)	BEGINNINGS AND ENDINGS OF METEOROLOGICAL PHENOMENA, REMARKS, NOTES, ETC. (13)	SL MNS (140)	SEA LEVEL PRESSURE (inches) (140)	TIME (E.S.T.)
00-01	83		SW	9					65	70	78		163	30.01	00-01
01-02	81		SW	10					67	69	77			30.01	01-02
02-03	80		W	10					67	68	76			30.00	02-03
03-04	78		W	9					71	68	74		159	30.00	03-04
04-05	78		NNW	9					71	68	74			30.01	04-05
05-06	78		NW	11					71	68	74			30.01	05-06
06-07	79		NW	9					69	68	75		166	30.02	06-07
07-08	81		NW	8					67	69	77			30.03	07-08
08-09	85		NW	6					66	70	79			30.03	08-09
09-10	88		NW	6					56	70	80		173	30.04	09-10
10-11	92		NNW	7					51	71	82			30.05	10-11
11-12	96		N	6					39	67	83			30.04	11-12
12-13	98		NW	7					31	62	83		165	30.03	12-13
13-14	98		NW	10					35	66	83			30.01	13-14
14-15	98		N	8					38	68	84			30.01	14-15
15-16	99		NW	8					34	66	84		163	30.01	15-16
16-17	97		W	7					38	67	83			30.01	16-17
17-18	93		NNW	6					41	66	81			30.01	17-18
18-19	88		N	7					50	67	80		166	30.02	18-19
19-20	86		NNW	5					50	65	78			30.03	19-20
20-21	86		NW	4					50	65	78			30.05	20-21
21-22	86		NW	4					48	64	78		163	30.07	21-22
22-23	86		CALM						50	65	78			30.08	22-23
23-24	84		CALM						55	66	77			30.08	23-24
SUM				166											
AVER.			NW (PREVAILING)	6.9	88.4%										
MISC.			NW												

SYMBOLS USED IN COLUMN 8

A—HAIL	IP—ICE PELLETS	DL—DISTANT LIGHTNING
R—RAIN	L—DRIZZLE	ZL—FREEZING DRIZZLE
S—SNOW	T—THUNDERSTORM	ZR—FREEZING RAIN

U.S. DEPARTMENT OF COMMERCE
NATIONAL OCEANIC AND ATMOSPHERIC ADMINISTRATION
NATIONAL WEATHER SERVICE

SURFACE WEATHER OBSERVATIONS
DAILY RECORD

STATION: **NEW YORK, N.Y.** Central Park   DATE: **Tuesday, July 19, 1977**

TO CONVERT LIST TO GMT   ADD **1** hr.   SUBTRACT **0** hr.

TIME (E.S.T.) (1)	TEMP. (°F) (2)	PRECIP-ITATION (inches) (3)	WIND DIRECTION (4)	WIND SPEED (M.P.H.) (5)	SUNSHINE (Minutes) (6)	SKY COVER (Scale 0-10) (7)	WEATHER (8)	PEAK GUST 20 MPH OR MORE (9)	REL. HUMIDITY (%) (10)	DEW POINT (11)	-T H- (12)	BEGINNINGS AND ENDINGS OF METEOROLOGICAL PHENOMENA; REMARKS, NOTES, ETC. (13)	V.L.P MBS	SEA LEVEL PRESSURE (inches) (14)	TIME (E.S.T.)
00-01	84		NE	7					55	66	77		180	30.06	00-01
01-02	81		NE	7					56	64	75			30.06	01-02
02-03	80		CALM	6					60	65	75			30.06	02-03
03-04	79		CALM						60	64	74		180	30.06	03-04
04-05	78		G.LM						60	63	73			30.06	04-05
05-06	78		CALM						60	63	73			30.06	05-06
06-07	80		NE	4					60	65	75		183	30.07	06-07
07-08	86		J	3					52	66	78			30.07	07-08
08-09	91		NNW	4					47	68	81			30.06	08-09
09-10	94		NNV	6					43	67	82		176	30.05	09-10
10-11	98		SW	8					37	62	84			30.03	10-11
11-12	99		SW	10					30	61	83			30.02	11-12
12-13	102		SW	8					26	61	84		163	30.01	12-13
13-14	102		SW	10					29	64	85			29.99	13-14
14-15	102		SW	9					28	63	84			29.98	14-15
15-16	100		SW	9					30	63	83		146	29.96	15-16
16-17	99		SW	10					26	58	82			29.97	16-17
17-18	96		SW	10					32	61	81			29.97	17-18
18-19	92		SW	9					40	65	81		146	29.96	18-19
19-20	89		SW	10					44	64	79			29.96	19-20
20-21	87		SW	7					42	61	77			29.97	20-21
21-22	85		SW	5					45	61	76		149	29.97	21-22
22-23	85		NW	6					45	61	76			29.97	22-23
23-24	84		NW	6					48	62	78			29.98	23-24
SUM				154	POSS 0.82 %										
AVER.			PREVAIL WIND	6.4											
MISC.			SW												

SYMBOLS USED IN COLUMN 8

A-HAIL	IP-ICE PELLETS	DL-DISTANT LIGHTNING
R-RAIN	L-DRIZZLE	ZL-FREEZING DRIZZLE
S-SNOW	T-THUNDERSTORM	ZR-FREEZING RAIN

WS FORM B-16 NY
(9-75)

SURFACE WEATHER OBSERVATIONS
DAILY RECORD

U.S. DEPARTMENT OF COMMERCE
NATIONAL OCEANIC AND ATMOSPHERIC ADMINISTRATION
NATIONAL WEATHER SERVICE

STATION NEW YORK, N.Y. Central Park   DATE Thursday, July 21, 1977

TO CONVERT LST TO GMT ADD 1 hrs. SUBTRACT 0 hrs.

TIME (E.S.T.) (1)	TEMPERATURE (°F) (2)	PRECIPITATION (Inches) (3)	WIND DIRECTION (4)	WIND SPEED (M.P.H.) (5)	SUNSHINE (Minutes) (6)	SKY COVER (Scale 0-10) (7)	WEATHER (8)	PEAK GUST 20 MPH OR MORE (9)	RELATIVE HUMIDITY (9)	DEW POINT (10)	T H I (11)	BEGINNINGS AND ENDINGS OF METEOROLOGICAL PHENOMENA, REMARKS, NOTES, ETC. (12)	SLP was	SEA LEVEL PRESSURE (Inches)	TIME (E.S.T.)
00:01	86			7					72	70	76		125	29.90	00.01
01:02	79		SSW	6					77	71	75			29.90	01.02
02:03	78		SSW	5					80	71	77			29.89	02.03
03:04	79		SSW	4					77	71	75		125	29.90	03.04
04:05	79		SSW	5					77	71	75			29.90	04.05
05:06	80		SW	5					74	71	77			29.91	05.06
06:07	81		SW	4					72	71	77		129	29.91	06.07
07:08	85		SW	4					67	72	79			29.90	07.08
08:09	89		W	4					61	74	82			29.89	08.09
09:10	94		SW	5					53	74	84		119	29.88	09.10
10:11	97		SW	5					44	71	85			29.88	10.11
11:12	101		SW	6					38	71	86			29.85	11.12
12:13	102		WNW	9					35	69	86		126	29.65	12.13
13:14	104		SW	6					32	68	87			29.82	13.14
14:15	103		SW	12					34	69	86			29.79	14.15
15:16	102		SW	10					35	69	86		078	29.76	15.16
16:17	99		N	12					40	70	85			29.77	16.17
17:18	95		N	15					45	70	83			29.76	17.18
18:19	92		NNW	15					44	67	81		85	29.78	18.19
19:20	87		NW	7					45	63	78			29.81	19.20
20:21	85		NW	11					50	64	77			29.84	20.21
21:22	84		NW	10					50	63	77		106	29.85	21.22
22:23	83		N	6					55	65	76			29.84	22.23
23:24	82		NNE	5					59	66	76			29.84	23.24
SUM				183											
AVER.		PREVAILING SW	7.6	88%											
MISC.															

SYMBOLS USED IN COLUMN 8

A—HAIL	IP—ICE PELLETS	AL—DISTANT LIGHTNING
R—RAIN	L—DRIZZLE	ZL—FREEZING DRIZZLE
S—SNOW	T—THUNDERSTORM	ZR—FREEZING RAIN

at 5,000 BTU/110 Volts on the East wall, by the master bedroom. The air conditioners, which are thermostatically controlled, were set at about 75°F and left undisturbed running continuously day and night for the duration of the test. Since during part of that time, the air conditioner's compressor (the part of the air conditioner that actually does the work to cool, which is what uses the most energy) was working and some time it was not (the unit serving as a circulatory device only, which, comparatively, does not use much electricity), the electricity consumption cannot be calculated based on wattage ratings only. Therefore, meter readings were taken at 8 a.m. and 8 p.m. The difference was then decreased by a predetermined standard amount representing the electricity required to run the permanent appliances such as the refrigerator, freezer, clocks, etc.

Precautions were taken to make sure that no other large appliance was used during the test, thereby ensuring that the electricity so calculated was indeed due to the air conditioner's consumption only. Since the temperature in the living area was always maintained at 75°F, a higher electric consumption therefore means that the compressor was working for a longer period of time.

Temperature was measured with calibrated thermometers in three spots:

1) outside air (in the shade)

2) attic air

3) roof (inside surface).

The thermometer used to measure the temperature of the roof was taped to the inside (plywood) surface with heavy-duty duct tape, criss-crossed several times over the bulb, to ensure that the temperature shown was as close as possible to that of the roof, minimizing the cooling effect of the attic air.

All the temperatures recorded were plotted on graphs, shown in Figures 33, 34, 35, and 36. To make it easier to find out which curve belongs to which thermometer, we will designate them by the following symbols:

www.KnowledgePublications.com

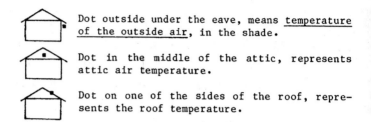

Dot outside under the eave, means <u>temperature of the outside air</u>, in the shade.

Dot in the middle of the attic, represents attic air temperature.

Dot on one of the sides of the roof, represents the roof temperature.

In Figure 33, showing the temperature for the conditions of no LEC and no fan, we can see clearly the tremendous heat buildup in the roof, and, slightly lower, the attic air. Both are much higher than the outside temperature. Note that when the sun goes down, starting at about 6 p.m., the roof cools faster than the attic air. This is simply because the roof, being a good absorber of energy, is also a good emitter. Once the external source of radiation decreases in intensity (sun going down), the emission takes over. Air, on the other hand, is slow to get heated and slow in giving up this heat.

Figure 34 shows the temperatures with no LEC, but with the attic fan on. The result is clear: the temperature in the attic does not get as high as in Figure 33, and since the air is renewed, the temperature goes down proportionately. Note that the outside temperature on the day when the test in Figure 34 was performed was about 5 degrees lower than that in Figure 33. Accordingly, the peak roof temperature is slightly lower. Although this is a slight advantage for the attic fan, its beneficial effect is undeniable.

But now let us see the effect of LEC in Figures 35 (without the attic fan) and 36 (with the attic fan). WOW! The temperature of the attic <u>AND THE TEMPERATURE OF THE ROOF</u> are almost identical to that of the outside air! (And, incidentally, when the test in Figure 36 was run, it happened to be the hottest day of the series). Since the roof is not hot, the attic air does not get hot. So, the attic fan does not help one way or the other.

Now let us examine how did the air conditioners in the living area see all this.

The use of the attic fan resulted in a meritorious 10 percent economy. But using LEC <u>without</u> the attic fan resulted in over 40 percent economy! Using LEC with the attic fan was less efficient simply because the fan was consuming electricity but contributing nothing to the cooling.

114

TABLE 7

	WITHOUT LEC		WITH LEC	
	without attic fan	with attic fan	without attic fan	with attic fan
kWh used @ $0.06/kWh	55.2 $3.31	49.8 $2.99	25.3 $1.52	27.9 $1.67
water used, cu ft @ $.004/cu ft	–	–	100 $0.40	100 $0.40
Total Cost	$3.31	$2.99	$1.92	$2.07
Economy (vs no LEC/no fan) $	0	0.32	1.39	1.24
Percent		9.7	41.2	37.5

These savings, expressed in dollar terms are impressive enough. But look at the kilowatt-hour figures! LEC resulted in over 50 percent savings in electricity consumption! You may get a better idea of the significance of this figure by reading again Section 2, "Cooling and Energy." More on this later.

Needless to say, these values apply to the conditions described. The factors involved are so numerous, that it is impossible to forecast exact results for other houses. Other situations may produce higher, lower, or equal savings. For example, in a house that is super-insulated, the effect of LEC is likely to be smaller. But that case is an exception. The opposite is much more common, and that will result in higher savings. Also, the test with LEC was run without a temperature control valve. Incorporating this device would result in lower water usage and cost.

Savings may vary from house to house. Cost figures may change. But the usefulness and practicality of the LEC system has been categorically demonstrated.

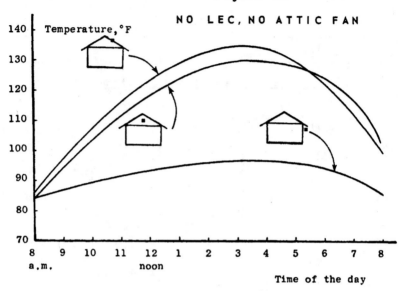

Figure 33

NO LEC, NO ATTIC FAN

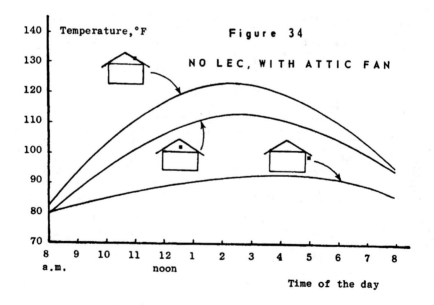

Figure 34

NO LEC, WITH ATTIC FAN

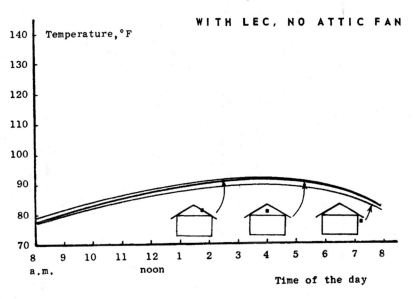

Figure 35

WITH LEC, NO ATTIC FAN

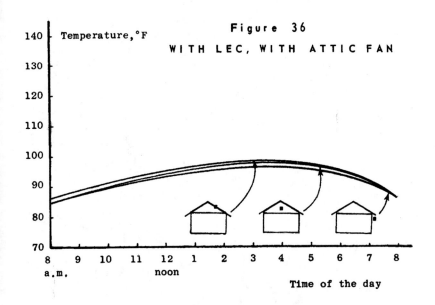

Figure 36

WITH LEC, WITH ATTIC FAN

Utilities may shut off

your air con'

During hot summer
in the near fu⁺
may find ⁺'
cond⁺'

Disaster predicted by T V A chief

the
⁺r
'cted
'aces

The
nat'
c⁺

Striking coal miners ignore back-to-work order

Power conservation urged

Public Utilities Commissior OK's electric rate hike

25

Test Your House

or   Prove it to Yourself

THE BEST WAY to determine the benefits of using the LEC method in your specific case is to run tests in your own home. To do this, just follow step-by-step the details described in the previous section. Of course, you will have to adapt the technique to the particular home.

You should make accurate temperature measurements in several places of the house. Thermometers used in photographic laboratories are adequate; those used for color processing are best. Make sure all of them show exactly the same temperature by placing them in a bucket of crushed ice, and reading the temperature after a few minutes. The temperature should be the same in all thermometers. Repeat in lukewarm water. If the thermometers do not show the exact same temperature, you still can use them: just tie on a label, put a number, and remember to correct the reading before recording the temperature.

In the following pages you will find blank forms that will enable you to self-direct the test, record results orderly, and calculate your savings.

DATA COLLECTION FORM

Date:	Conditions		Meter Readings		
	LEC ☐			Initial	Final
	Attic Fan ☐	Electricity			
	Air Conditioner ☐	Water			

Time:		Temperature in:				Relative Humidity
		Living Area	Attic Air	Roof	Outside Air	
a.m.	8					
	9					
	10					
	11					
p.m.	12					
	1					
	2					
	3					
	4					
	5					
	6					
	7					
	8					

120

DATA COLLECTION FORM

Date:	Conditions		Meter Readings		
				Initial	Final
	LEC ☐				
	Attic Fan ☐		Electricity		
	Air Conditioner ☐		Water		

Time:		Temperature in:				Relative Humidity
		Living Area	Attic Air	Roof	Outside Air	
a.m.	8					
	9					
	10					
	11					
p.m.	12					
	1					
	2					
	3					
	4					
	5					
	6					
	7					
	8					

121

DATA COLLECTION FORM

Date:	Conditions		Meter Readings		
	LEC ☐			Initial	Final
	Attic Fan ☐		Electricity		
	Air Conditioner ☐		Water		

Time:		Temperature in:				Relative Humidity
		Living Area	Attic Air	Roof	Outside Air	
a.m.	8					
	9					
	10					
	11					
p.m.	12					
	1					
	2					
	3					
	4					
	5					
	6					
	7					
	8					

DATA COLLECTION FORM

Date:	Conditions		Meter Readings		
	LEC ☐			Initial	Final
	Attic Fan ☐	Electricity			
	Air Conditioner ☐	Water			

Time:		Temperature in:				Relative Humidity
		Living Area	Attic Air	Roof	Outside Air	
a.m.	8					
	9					
	10					
	11					
p.m.	12					
	1					
	2					
	3					
	4					
	5					
	6					
	7					
	8					

123

SUMMARY

	WITHOUT LEC		WITH LEC	
	without attic fan	with attic fan	without attic fan	with attic fan
Electricity used, kWh				
Price of electricity, ¢/kWh				
Cost of electricity				
Water used, cu.ft.				
Price of water,¢/cu.ft.				
Cost of water				
Total cost				

26

Special Cases

or   **Cathedrals and Schools**

THE USEFULNESS OF LATENT EVAPORATIVE COOLING has been demonstrated, with numbers, in an average home. This home had reasonably good original insulation, to which more insulation was added, prompted by energy costs and availability. It is easy to imagine the frustration felt by homeowners who can't reinsulate. Well, of course, any house *can* be reinsulated if you want it hard enough. But in many cases this would represent major alterations, with consequent high costs.

For example, let us take that very common case where the living and dining rooms have a cathedral ceiling. This area does not have an attic where insulation can be added. In the sense of heat transmission, the living and dining rooms <u>are</u> the attic, because that is where the heat absorbed by the roof will go first, with nothing else to stop it. Reinsulation would mean adding a new layer of material from the inside, and then a new ceiling under it. Some project! LEC is truly a salvation for homes with cathedral ceilings.

A somewhat similar situation is encountered in certain Cape Cod models, where the attic is largely a living level. Alterations, therefore, would involve wrecking finished rooms.

Houses with flat or Mansard roofs have a different situation. Since water will not flow into a thin film as it does on a gable roof, puddles will be formed, and evaporation will slow down. The solution here is to have a thermostatically-controlled

125

valve, as described in the section on Regulation, so that the water spray is stopped as soon as the temperature of the roof drops to a predetermined level. The key is to have accurate temperature control, and this means sensitive instrumentation, which the home-owner may or may not be able or willing to buy.

However, this brings us to another potential use of LEC, where the building owner *can* afford refined instrumentation. These are the industrial and institutional owners. Thousands upon thousands of acres of flat-roofed offices, shopping centers, light manufacturing plants, research laboratories, warehouses, schools, hospitals, motels, and miscellaneous other buildings are scattered across the country, their pitch black toppings avidly sucking every bit of energy that hits them. And, through a mechanism entirely similar to that described for a home, that heat finds its way through the building's components to the living area, and then to the thermostat of that kilowatt-guzzling air conditioner. Many of these buildings are used almost exclusively during daylight hours, when sunshine and heat are higher, while many homes are unoccupied during the day. This is why institutional use of Latent Evapora-tive Cooling would make such an important contribution to energy saving.

Until now, we have not talked about walls. Obviously, LEC *can* be used on walls. However, the rapid fall of water on a vertical surface, and the relatively low energy uptake of walls make it unattractive. Besides, provisions should be made to bypass windows, since constant running of water would be annoying. A possible exception could be a brick windowless wall facing South. In this case, the red or brownish brick color would make a good energy absorber, and the porous nature of the material would improve the contact with water. Thermostatic control would be essential.

Finally, we should mention those cases where LEC could provide an adequate degree of cooling by itself, without any air conditioning. In extreme northern locations, with very short hot seasons, and especially near large bodies of water which act as temperature moderators, making very hot days rare, cooling by LEC only might prove entirely adequate. Another possibility, this time in the institutional area, would be in warehouses such as for storage of certain perishable products or flammable materials, where only extremely high temperatures are to be avoided. The possibilities are enormous. Merely an awareness that the system exists and is workable, will generate innumerable ideas for saving money, electricity, and fuels.

126

27

What do Others Say ?

HAVING READ THIS BOOK up to this point, I grant you the right to ask "But, if all this about Latent Evaporative Cooling is such an effective, economical and sure-fire thing, how come nobody has thought of it before?"

Well, the fact is that a lot of people have not only thought about it, but have actually used it. The first time I saw LEC used in home cooling, was in a form quite different from the one presented here. It was in a place that sure can use it, because it is the hottest spot in the U.S.: Death Valley, California, where the temperature may reach 140°F. One of the many oddities of this magnificent National Monument is Scotty's Castle, an amazing mansion built in the 1920's by an eccentric cowboy turned millionaire. In some rooms, there is a stone wall with water cascading down in the form of a thin film. As the tour guide will tell you, the evaporation of water cools the room. Of course, a problem here is that the humidity indoors will keep rising to the point of becoming unbearable.

There have been many other similar forms of application of the LEC principle. Figure 37 shows a system to cool outside air which is sucked through wet pads, where water evaporates, cooling the air, which is then pumped through the house. This system also has the shortcoming of indoor humidity buildup.

An attempt to solve this problem is the two-stage evaporative cooler. Water evaporating is used to cool a heat exchanger

127

through which the house's air is force-circulated. As you can see, this method requires a lot of hardware, the cost of which will be difficult to justify. There have been also numerous patents issued utilizing Evaporative Cooling for all kinds of purposes, including roofs, as in the facsimiles shown. Most of these patents, whose legal 17-year term of validity expired long ago, were primarily refinements of the regulator portion of the system. (Physical principles cannot be patented--only specific ways to use them can).

So after reviewing what other people have done, maybe we ought to reword the opening question of this section like this: "If Latent Evaporative Cooling is such an effective, economical, and sure-fire thing, how come no more people are using it?" The answer is simply because until now it was not needed. It is like asking "If insulation is such an effective way to save energy, how come houses were built with so little insulation?" Likewise, simply because until now, more was not needed. But needed they are now. Both insulation and LEC. There is an additional comment as to why LEC has not been used more. And probably it can be summed up best by the statement by S. David Freeman, Director of the Ford Foundation Energy Policy Project: "We have a National Energy Policy, and it's basically one of promotion, of pushing the product." Pushing the product. Pushing the profitable product. $3 worth of electricity will generate more profits than 40 cents worth of water. A $300 air conditioner will generate more profits than $30 worth of hoses. And it's easier to use: plug in and turn on. Easier, until you turn it on and it does not run.

Figure 37

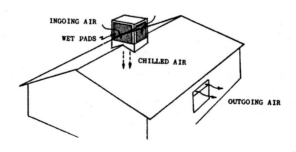

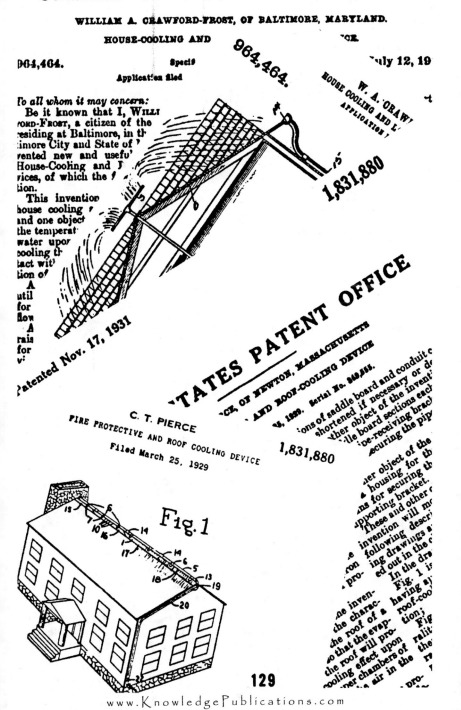

UNITED STATES PATENT OFFICE.

WILLIAM A. CRAWFORD-FROST, OF BALTIMORE, MARYLAND.

HOUSE-COOLING AND

964,464.

D64,464.   Specif   July 12, 19

Application filed

To all whom it may concern:
Be it known that I, WILLI
rond-Frost, a citizen of the
esiding at Baltimore, in th
imore City and State of '
vented new and usefu'
House-Cooling and J
rices, of which the '
tion.
This invention
house cooling '
and one object
the temperat
water upor
cooling th
tact wit'
tion of
A
util
for
flow
A
rais
for
v'

Patented Nov. 17, 1931

964,464.

W. A. 'ORAW'
HOUSE COOLING AND L
APPLICATION '

1,831,880

UNITED STATES PATENT OFFICE

C. T. PIERCE
FIRE PROTECTIVE AND ROOF COOLING DEVICE
Filed March 25, 1929

CE, OF NEWTON, MASSACHUSETTS
AND ROOF-COOLING DEVICE
V., 1929. Serial No. 349,355.

1,831,880

ons of saddle board and conduit c
shortened if necessary or de
her object of the inventi
lle board sections each
pe-receiving brack
ecuring the pip

er object of the
housing for th
ns for securing th
pporting bracket.
These and other
invention will m
following drawings a
ing drawings
ed out in the c
In the dr
Fig. 1 is
having a'
roof-coo
tion;
Fig
ralit
the
r'
pro-

ne inven-
the charac-
the roof of a
that the evap-
o the roof will pro-
cooling effect upon
er chambers of
air in the

Fig. 1

129

Patented Jan. 26, 1937

2,069,1

UNITED STATES PATENT OFFICE

2,069,150

ROOF COOLING DEVICE

Leonard H. Holder, Washington, D. C.

Application July 22, 1935, Serial No. 32,613

2 Claims. (Cl. 299—141)

The present invention relates to means for cooling roofs of buildings and the like, large and small, and has for an object the provision of a nozzle which may be connected to a source of water supply to maintain a roof and the upper floor or floors of the relatively cool under

Another feature of the provide a stru cut

Jan. 26, 1937.

2,069,150

L. H. HOLDER

ROOF COOLING DEVICE

Filed July 22, 1935

3 Sheets—Sheet 1

Patented Dec. 16, 1941

UNITED STATES PATENT OFFICE

2,266,321

2,266,32

ROOF COOLING DEVICE

Leonard H. Holder, Washington, D. C.

Application June 4, 1940, Serial No. 338,811

17 Claims. (Cl. 62—6)

present invention relates to the prevention ssive heat accumulation in exposed sur- ch as roofs and contemplates particularly rolled dissipation of heat through the latent heat of vaporization of a suit- such as water. sent invention more particularly con- the complete utilization of the entire evaporative cooling effect available he absorption of heat by exposed roof in particularly comprehends the absorbed heat in the t energy has ly int

cooling the water. In short, from an initially high roof cooling efficiency, the action progres- aively and rapidly approaches the condition of low evaporative cooling efficiency wherein reliance must necessarily be placed cooling effect of the water coolant is not available tion, cooling also.

www.KnowledgePublications.com

ed Mar. 2, 1948

2,437,156

UNITED STATES PATENT OFFICE

2,437,156

METHOD AND APPARATUS FOR COOLING BY EVAPORATION

Albion N. Frick, Los Angeles, Calif., assignor to Frederick G. Bradbury, Los Angeles, Calif.

Application July 11, 1942, Serial No. 650,625

3 Claims. (Cl. 62—6)

1

vention relates to the method and valve
means for cooling by evaporation and
rticularly to the operation of ——
such as are used for —
for cooling —

.. A suitabl—

2,437,156

March 2, 1948.

A. N. FRICK

METHOD AND APPARATUS FOR COOLING BY EVAPORATION

Filed July 11, 1942

2 Sheets—Sheet 2

Dec. 16, 1941.

L. H. HOLDER

ROOF COOLING DEVICE

Filed June 4, 1940

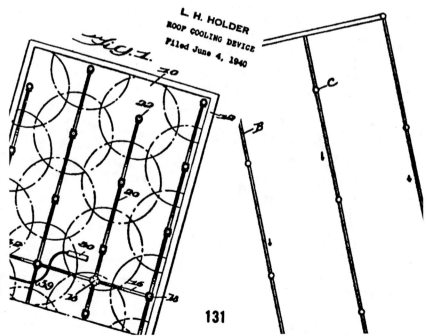

Fig. 1.

131

''TED STATES PATENT OFFICE

May 9, 1950

: 2,506,938

~OOF COOLING SYSTEM

~~ray, Pasadena, Calif.

~ Serial No. 744,783

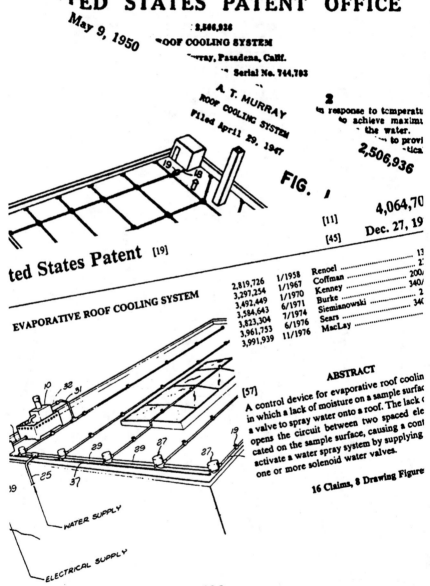

A. T. MURRAY
ROOF COOLING SYSTEM
Filed April 29, 1967

2

in response to temperatu
to achieve maximu
the water.
to provi
tica

2,506,936

FIG. /

4,064,70

[11]

[45]   Dec. 27, 19

ted States Patent [19]

EVAPORATIVE ROOF COOLING SYSTEM

2,819,726	1/1958	Renoel 13
3,297,254	1/1967	Coffman 2
3,492,449	1/1970	Kenney 200/
3,584,643	6/1971	Burke 340/
3,823,304	7/1974	Siemianowski 2
3,961,753	6/1976	Sears 340
3,991,939	11/1976	MacLay ....

ABSTRACT

[57]
A control device for evaporative roof coolin
in which a lack of moisture on a sample surfac
a valve to spray water onto a roof. The lack c
opens the circuit between two spaced ele
cated on the sample surface, causing a cont
activate a water spray system by supplying
one or more solenoid water valves.

16 Claims, 8 Drawing Figure

WATER SUPPLY

ELECTRICAL SUPPLY

28

Conservation of Resources

or   There is a difference

THERE IS A GOOD CHANCE that throughout our discussion of Latent Evaporative Cooling you were concerned about the large amounts of water that would take to run it.

We have shown tables of water costs. We have also seen results of actual house tests which demonstrate that the water cost to the homeowner is much lower than that of electricity required to extract an equivalent amount of heat with an air conditioner. And yet, it is very probable that somebody would still be calling LEC a "waste of a precious resource." So, let's analyze this issue.

Indeed water is a precious natural resource. It is essential to maintain life. And nothing else will work for that. But this is a misleading argument. Very little of the enormous amounts of water used every day goes to maintain life.

Regarding cooling applications, let us compare the major features of Air Conditioning and Latent Evaporative Cooling.

Air conditioning seems simple because we are accustomed to see and use it, but really it is a Rube Goldberg sequence of inefficient steps. Latent Evaporative Cooling, on the other hand, is an _in-situ_ (in-place), _machine-less_, _efficient_, _nonpolluting_ conversion of energy.

Air conditioning can attain practically any desired temperature, depending only on the equipment used. LEC, on the

133

other hand, has limitations imposed by atmospheric conditions. For this reason, air conditioning unquestionably will continue to be a required piece of equipment for home cooling. The point is, LEC can do a large portion of the job done by air conditioning, at a lower expense in terms of dollars and energy used. Therefore, from an efficiency standpoint, LEC should be the cooling workhorse, and air conditioning the emergency device to take up the job beyond the capability of LEC. Nowadays, of course, inefficient air conditioning does the whole job, and that's why we are in such a pickle. If somebody says that LEC is a waste of water, it is probably because he actually sees the water flowing. When one turns on the air conditioner, the electricity is not seen, nor is the chain of inefficiencies. Out of sight, out of mind.

But if all this were not enough, now we come to the most basic, fundamental, and important difference between air conditioning and LEC. When coal or fuel oil are burned, they are chemically converted into carbon dioxide and water, which will remain in that condition for the rest of eternity. Combustion is a one-shot deal, which uses in an instant the result of millions of years of Nature's work.

Latent Evaporative Cooling does not destroy anything. Nothing is chemically changed. Water evaporated from your roof will drift, purer than before, to the next cloud, from which it will come down in the next week's rain, and flow down the river, so your utility will collect it again, and sell it again to you, this time maybe to cook your spaghetti dinner. Thus, we arrive at the golden feature of LEC:

> **LATENT EVAPORATIVE COOLING OPERATES ON A RENEWABLE NATURAL RESOURCE.**

So, putting all of this in a summary form we have:

TABLE 8

	Air Conditioning	LEC
Steps	1) Obtain fuel (mine coal or pump and purify oil).	1) Collect and purify water.
	2) Burn fuel to generate heat.	2) Deliver to houses.
	3) Use the heat to generate steam.	3) Spray on roof removes heat.
	4) Use steam to power a generator.	
	5) Transmit electricity.	
	6) Electricity powers a motor.	
	7) Motor operates the compressor and fan.	
	8) Compressor and fan remove heat.	
Efficiency of the Chain (From basic sources to final heat removal)	Low	High
Minimum Temperature Attainable	Practically any	Has limitations
Change in the Energy Source	Chemical, Irreversible	Physical, Reversible
Availability of Active Agent	Limited	Renewable

135

29

Fuel Replacement Value

or   It won't burn , but...

IF WATER (through LEC) can do part of the cooling job done by electricity (through air conditioning), and electricity is produced by fuel-powered generators, water can save fuel. We can calculate, therefore, a theoretical fuel replacement value of water.

You may recall that in Section 20, we figured that when a half-gallon of water evaporates, it removes an amount of heat roughly equivalent to that removed by a 5,000 BTU air conditioner in one hour. If this air conditioner has an EER (Energy-Efficiency Ratio) of 5, it will require 1,000 watts for operation, or one kilowatt every hour, or 1 kWh.

From energy-conversion tables, we can calculate that one kilowatt-hour is theoretically equivalent to about 3,000 BTU (this is energy equivalence--do not confuse it with the rating of the air conditioner, which is a heat-removing value). Now, we have seen that energy conversion in a power plant is far from perfect: the net efficiency, from heat value of the fuel to the electricity output is about 30 percent. This means that the 1 kWh needed to run our air conditioner (roughly equivalent to 3,000 BTU) comes from about a 10,000 BTU input. We can obtain this heat by burning coal, fuel oil, gas, etc. The following tables gives the heat produced by several fuels:

137

TABLE 9

Heat Geneated By the Combustion of Various Fuels

Coal: approximately   15,000 BTU/lb

Fuel oil: approximately   18,000 BTU/lb

Gas: approximately   1,000 BTU/cubic foot

Therefore, depending on how we run our electric plant, to generate that 1 kWh it may take about 2/3 pound of coal, 1/2 pound of fuel oil, or 10 cubic feet of gas.

Since this calculation was derived from a half gallon of water, the theoretical fuel value per gallon of water is obtained simply by doubling these figures. Therefore:

TO OBTAIN BY AIR CONDITIONING THE COOLING POWER EQUIVALENT TO EVAPORATING ONE GALLON OF WATER, WE MUST BURN APPROXIMATELY:
ONE AND ONE-HALF POUNDS OF COAL
OR
ONE POUND OF FUEL OIL
OR TWENTY CUBIC FEEET OF GAS.

These are impressive figures indeed.

If we continue this comparison and find the fuel value of common everyday uses of water, we would get some results ranging from sobering to hilarious.

Example: Books on lawn care often recommend watering at the rate of one inch per week. A few minutes' work with your calculator will show you that this comes to about 27,000 gallons of water per acre. Therefore, this represents, according to the table above, 27,000 pounds (about 3600 gallons) of fuel oil.

Example: Every time you flush the toilet, you let down the drain the equivalent of about one-third of a gallon of fuel oil.

And so on. Of course, these equivalent values, although

138

accurate, are not directly replaceable: air conditioning removes
heat directly from the room, while LEC as described here, takes it
from the roof.   (LEC could take it from the room also, were it not
because of the high resulting humidity.)   The purpose of this
exercise is simple: to emphasize once more the great money and
fuel savings possibilities opened by LEC.

The whole world is looking for new energy resources.   If
a new oil well is found, it's front-page news.   Yet, we have a
partial oil replacement raining somewhere around us practically
every day, and we literally let it go down the drain.

It is time to use it.   And, if it becomes scarce, it is
time to use it more wisely, just like any other form of energy.
Just like solar energy, LEC is most useful in small-temperature-
difference applications.   And, just like solar energy, it is
practically inexhaustible: all we have to do is to desalinate
seawater.

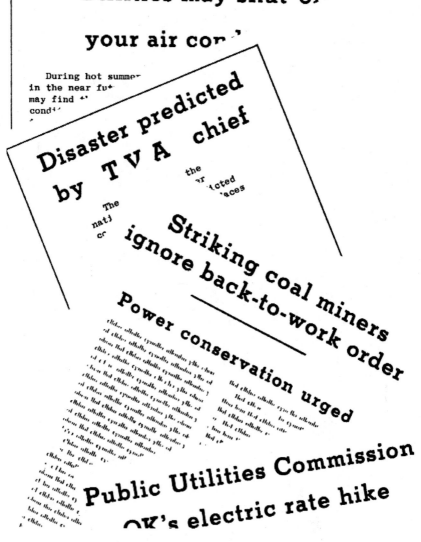

Utilities may shut off

your air con...

During hot summer
in the near fu...
may find ...
cond...

Disaster predicted
by T V A chief

the
...icted
...aces

The
nat...
c...

Striking coal miners
ignore back-to-work order

Power conservation urged

Public Utilities Commission

OK's electric rate hike

30

Conclusion

or   **DO IT !**

WE HAVE SAID that the whole problem of air conditioning can be reduced to the fact that heat comes into the house, so it has to be pumped out again. Having read this book, you are equipped now to understand something that probably would not have made any sense to you earlier: Latent Evaporative Cooling works so well largely because it reduces drastically the amount of heat coming into the house by absorbing it at the point of higher concentration: the surface of the roof. If the roof is not hot, the attic does not get hot. The attic fan is therefore eliminated. Additionally, LEC has the capacity to actually cool the house below the temperature of the surrounding air, a feature that no attic fan can provide.

While air conditioning is an inefficient contraption that works on electricity generated by irreversible combustion of increasingly scarce fuels, LEC works by an efficient, machine-less, non-polluting, reversible physical change in the most abundant substance in the world.

As with any new development that changes established ways, some people will do nothing but find problems, real or fictitious, with LEC. An argument sure to come up is "If everybody would use LEC, there would not be enough water to go around."

This argument is like saying "If everybody would turn on their air conditioner at the same time, there won't be enough juice to go around." Well --- sounds familiar, doesn't it? This is

141

true, it happens today; you know it, and still you bet your and your family's comfort on a system that is already overburdened, and likely to get much worse soon.

The point is, today **NOT** everybody is using LEC, while everybody **IS** turning on their air conditioners. Therefore, your chances for having water available are considerably better than for having electricity available. And the utility cannot shut off your water. And there are no miners to go on strike.

Because of the savings in air conditioning, a clear fuel equivalence value may be calculated for water. This feature alone is likely to place LEC in a favored position against many other, much more dispensable uses of water, such as lawn care, car washing, and sidewalk sweeping.

The days of waste are over. In the future, all natural resources will have to be used more wisely. This means that each resource should be channeled to those applications where efficient, nondestructive, recyclable usage results. As the title of this book promises, L E C can save you money today, and energy for everybody's use tomorrow. Widespread use of LEC would be an excellent way (maybe the only way, in the short range) to ensure that everbody could use their air conditioner when really needed.

One final thought:

EVEN IF YOU ARE NOT PLANNING TO USE LEC REGULARLY, IT SURE WOULD MAKE A DARN GOOD, INEXPENSIVE STANDBY SYSTEM TO FALL BACK ON WHEN THE LIGHTS WILL GO OUT.

◆◆◆

142

About the author:
George S. Barton is a Materials Scientist
with long and rich experience. He has authored numerous works, and has lectured
widely here and abroad.As a homeowner, he
has endeavored to apply scientific principles and common sense in the search for
practical answers to the energy problem.